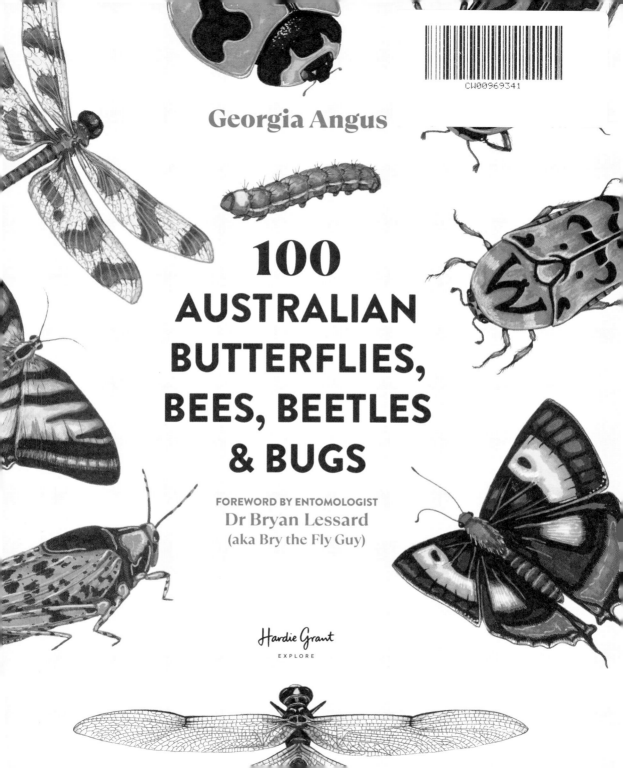

Georgia Angus

100 AUSTRALIAN BUTTERFLIES, BEES, BEETLES & BUGS

FOREWORD BY ENTOMOLOGIST
Dr Bryan Lessard
(aka Bry the Fly Guy)

Hardie Grant
EXPLORE

CONTENTS

FOREWORD

Australia is one of the world's biodiversity hotspots, with 70,000 of the 200,000 recorded native species being insects. *100 Australian Butterflies, Bees, Beetles & Bugs* is the perfect guide for anyone looking to learn more about Australia's charismatic insects. Enjoy identifying the next species you spot using the beautiful scientific illustrations and helpful descriptions.

As someone who discovered insects rather late at university, I wish I had a field guide like this as a kid to explore the entomological world around me. I remember looking at my first blow fly under the microscope. I was astounded by the shining metallic colours, detailed textures and morphological intricacies. I was hooked and dedicated my career to learning more about these important creatures. Some of my fondest memories from the field are from when I stood back and watched flies dance in a forest canopy. I was in awe of their incredible aerodynamics and unique personalities, features often unnoticed by hikers passing by.

Insects are the workhorses of the environment, providing essential ecosystem services free of charge. Despite their fundamental roles in nature, they are often misunderstood by many people. Native blow flies, beetles, moths and wasps have all pollinated Australian plants long before the European honeybee arrived on our shores. Recent studies have shown that even the 'pesky' blow fly can carry vast amounts of pollen. Today, Australian farmers are encouraging blow flies to pollinate their mango and avocado orchids. Food for thought the next time you're out to brunch.

Insects are a vital part of the food chain for hungry amphibians, birds, reptiles and small mammals. First Nations Peoples have recognised the high nutritional and cultural value of insects for tens of thousands of years. As Australia's first farmers and agricultural scientists, many Communities have eaten iconic native species like the bogong moth, green tree ant and Witjuti grub.

Insect larvae are remarkable nutrient recyclers on the forest floors and in the garden. They turn organic matter, like leaves, bark and animal excrement, into rich compost eaten by plants and fungi. Larvae have inspired Australian insect farmers to divert food waste from landfill and turn it into high protein feed. These sustainable farms are powered by black soldier fly larvae (*Hermetia illucens*), which you may have seen in your backyard compost. Turns out insects are doing their bit to help create the circular, low-impact agricultural systems of the future.

The time to nurture and protect our native insects is now. Australian biodiversity is facing increasing threats of climate change, deforestation and the introduction of invasive species. The 2019/2020 Black Summer bushfires decimated the habitat and populations of not just the cute and cuddly macrofauna like koalas, but also the understudied insects. It's likely that we lost species of insects in the bushfires before they were ever known to science, as scientists have identified only one-quarter of Australian insect species. We need help from the next generation of scientists, conservationists and citizen scientists to identify and protect our unique insect biodiversity long into the future.

Your passion and curiosity for Australian insects will pique after reading Georgia's book. This essential field guide will help you identify and appreciate our hard-working native insect species. It is the perfect companion to any citizen science app that will help you see, snap and share the species you find on your next outdoor adventure. You never know, you might even discover a species new to science!

Dr Bryan Lessard

Dr Bryan Lessard, better known as Bry the Fly Guy, is an award-winning Australian entomologist and science communicator. He is a world recognised dipterist and has worked at the CSIRO Australian National Insect Collection and Australian Biological Resources Study. Bryan has named 50 species of flies new to science, including the famous Beyoncé and RuPaul flies. These fabulous flies sparked a global conversation on the importance of flies and taxonomy, the science of naming and classifying species. Bryan is passionate about inspiring the next generation of scientist and has published a children's book Eyes On Flies *(2022). He is active on social media and a frequent guest on radio and television programs including* ABC News *and* BBC World News. *His research has also featured on* The Ellen DeGeneres Show *and* The Graham Norton Show.

INTRODUCTION

There is so much surreal beauty in the insect realm that can enrich your experience of the environment, if you only take the time to look. Discovering and learning about insects is rather like deep-ocean exploration – there are endless species and environments yet to be uncovered in the minute world of these amazing creatures. This sense of awe and fascination is what I want to share with you by offering this guide. The 100 insects featured in this book only scratch the surface, but I hope they spark your curiosity to know more.

My experience with insects began some years ago when my family decided to climb the Horn of Mount Buffalo on Taungurung Country to watch the sunset. It was windy and freezing, but we quickly forgot the temperature when we reached the top. From this point, Victoria's High Country stretched out around us, a kaleidoscope of ridgelines and peaks in every shade of blue. With some mid-air finger-walking, we could summit Mount Feathertop, Mount Bogong, Mount Mckay and the Fainters in the same minute. Passing a thermos between us in the disappearing light, we admired the mountains until the stars appeared. With the starlight came an immense fluttering noise. When we turned our torches upward, the night sky was thick with the furry bodies of thousands of bogong moths. The stars were blotted out, and I was overwhelmed with a sense of insignificance amongst the masses of insects taking flight. Experiencing the wonder of the moths on the mountain sent me down a research rabbit-hole.

In summer, bogong moths retreat from their northern feeding grounds to the southern Great Dividing Range. Here, near the cooler mountain summits, they can avoid the stress and moisture loss that comes from summer temperatures in the lowlands – that was why they were up on the Horn that night. After seeing out the hot months, the moths migrate north again to lay eggs and renew the cycle. A number of First Nations Peoples clan groups from as far as the coast would gather in the High Country during the hot seasons to feed on the moths, which are an excellent source of energy. The name 'bogong' itself is derived from the Dhuduroa word *bugung*, which describes the brown colour of the moth. In 2019, on Gunaikurnai Country in East Gippsland, a grindstone was found in a cave above the floodplains along with bogong moth remains approximately 2000 years old. Here was a physical record of a long connection between humans and insects – one marked by the seasonal gatherings where bogong moths were collected, cooked, and eaten or preserved for future times of scarcity. Learning the significance of these insects, I realised how lucky I had been to not only see a mass flight of bogong moths, but to stand right in the middle of it, feeling the soft patter of moths brushing against me.

Previously, I had never taken much interest in insects, beyond admiring a butterfly in the backyard, or running away from European wasps. But the bogong moths had sparked my curiosity. If this plain-looking moth has such an interesting ecological and cultural history, there must be many other Australian insects who have equally unique significance. I wanted to better understand the insect groups that are native to this country, and how they impact both humans and the environment.

I started by trying to learn how to ID different insect types. As it turns out, that is no simple mission. Entomology – the study of insects – is still unfolding as an area of research, with many insect species yet to be classified. At first I was overwhelmed by the enormous diversity of species as I read about the major insect orders. I remember finding out that there are 10,000 fly species in Australia alone. 10,000! You can't exactly send a group of researchers out to count all 10,000 fly species. This wild diversity is the case for many Australian insect groups – the numbers are astounding. There are approximately 2000 bee species, a growing 23,000 beetle species, approximately 400 butterfly species, approximately 20,000 moths, about 300 dragonflies and damselflies, and so on. And those are only species that have been described. These numbers will doubtless grow as entomologists discover yet more species. With every new group I encountered came wilder discoveries about the ingenious ways evolution has morphed these critters into survival machines.

Insects are often considered gross, dangerous, or a combination of the two. However, they are essential to our survival. Many insects are primary pollinators, not just European honey bees, but many native bees, flies, beetles, butterflies and moths are essential to both native ecosystems and also to many of our food crops. In other cases, insects act as essential pest control. For example, parasitic wasps can have a major impact on harmful fruit fly infestations. Insects also create products we readily use: honey and wax sourced from bees, silk from moths, clothing and food dyes from cochineal bugs, while insect proteins are even used for feed stock and human consumption. Beyond commercial uses, insects perform vital nutrient recycling in ecosystems by breaking down wood, waste and carcasses into available compounds for other organisms to use.

Like fungi and bacteria, they are the unseen pillars of forest ecosystems, allowing cycles to renew, and forging the path for other plants and animals to develop. They present an essential step in the food chain, as a primary food source for many other animals, including birds, some mammals, bats, fish, frogs, lizards and others. They also influence environmental conditions in various ways. Some Australian termites, for example, tunnel underground, gathering and breaking down vast swathes of grass and wood in their colonies, thus increasing the nutrient content of local soils. Their activity aerates the earth, and allows moisture to better penetrate

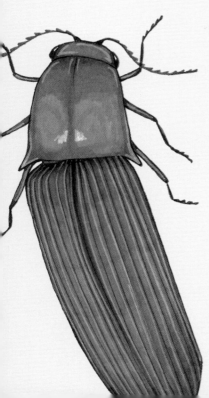

into the landscape and reducing run-off. Insects may be small, but they are collectively indispensable cogs in our ecosystems.

At the same time, we can appreciate insects for their elaborate charm. Their life strategies often lend them an almost poetic sensibility: fireflies communicate with light signals (produced by enzymes in their abdomen), and mantids seek mates by using chemical signatures that disperse through the night air. Magnetic termites reflect our celestial position within the alignment of their nest, while some butterfly chrysalises match the colours of their surrounds, as a natural mirror to their environment. Katydids and grasshoppers 'sing', wooing their lovers by rubbing a file against their wing, while the enigmatic hairy cicada communicates through silent vibrations, the last of its kind in the world. Some moths wear bee-costumes, some caterpillars beguile ants using sugary elixirs, and certain ants weave homes in tree canopies where they can live an entire life without setting a tiny foot on the ground. Predatory diving beetles can create their own scuba tanks, while water striders can walk across the surface of a lake, hunting prey. At a certain point, some part of me eventually surrendered to the fact that I can never know everything there is to know about insects. Isn't that a brilliant prospect?

This book will introduce you to 100 native Australian insects. I want you, my reader, to learn about Australian insects without having to study the scientific language of a hefty field guide. Hence, I have written this book to make insect descriptions accessible to you, and illustrated insects to show their beauty and detail, enabling you to spot and observe them in their habitats. I have also included suggestions for how to foster native insect life – be it by growing certain plants, creating habitat spaces, providing water, protecting local bush reserves, or sharing your passion for the natural world with others. I have created this book with the guidance of experienced entomologists, research papers, scientific field guides, and supplemented entries with personal observations where possible. While there is roughly an estimated 85,000 insect species in Australia, with more yet to be discovered, this first 100 will act as a stepping-stone to get you on your way to appreciating Australian insects.

SPIDER ANT

TEDDY BEAR BEE

DOUBLE-
DRUMMER
CICADA

ERCULES MOTH

YELLOW FLUTERER
DRAGONFLY

VELVET ANT

TIGER LONGICORN

STALK-
EYED FLY

JEWEL BEETLE

VARIABLE
LADYBIRD

HELIOTROPE
MOTH

HONEYBROWN BEETLE

CHOCOLATE ARGUS

JOSEPH'S
AT MOTH

GIANT RAINFOREST MANTID

BLUE ANT

GRANNY SMITH
CHRISTMAS BEETLE

BESS BEETLE

ALPINE METALLIC
COCKROACH

ANATOMY

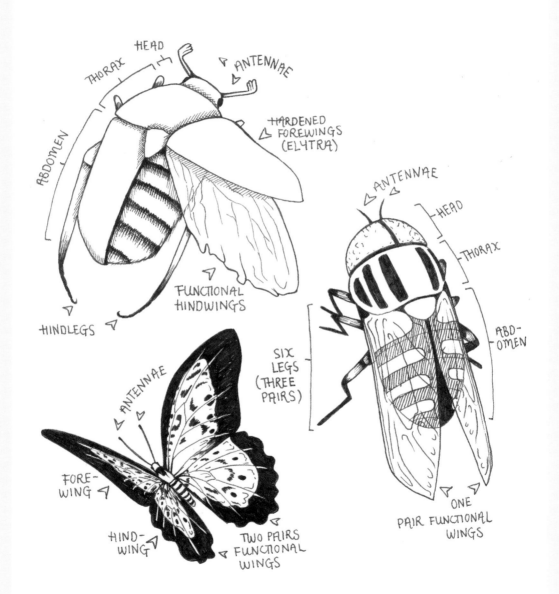

THORAX HEAD

ANTENNAE

HARDENED FOREWINGS (ELYTRA)

ABDOMEN

FUNCTIONAL HINDWINGS

HINDLEGS

ANTENNAE

HEAD

THORAX

ABDOMEN

SIX LEGS (THREE PAIRS)

ONE PAIR FUNCTIONAL WINGS

ANTENNAE

FORE-WING

HIND-WING

TWO PAIRS FUNCTIONAL WINGS

WHAT ARE INSECTS?

Insects are animals that are in the class Insecta, which is within the subphylum Hexapoda. Insects, while very diverse, have several things in common which can help you identify them.

Hexapoda roughly means 'six legs', and in keeping with the theme, all insects have six legs, made up of three pairs. Insects also have an external skeleton – a hardened outer 'shell' which protects their organs and gives their body structure. The exoskeleton can limit growth, so insects will go through moults and shed a layer of their exoskeleton to give them room to grow – similar to a snake shedding its skin.

Another consistent feature is that insects are ectothermic (cold-blooded) so, like reptiles, they rely on external warmth to increase their body temperature and allow them to become active. This is one of the reasons why insect activity becomes much more abundant in spring and summer – all those ladybirds have just been waiting for enough sun to warm up their little biological engines. Most insects have some form of wings (not always functional, and in some cases absent), and they have a segmented body, comprised of a head, thorax, and abdomen. While this is usually obvious when looking at an insect, certain species, such as female bark cockroaches (*see* p.135), have different shaped pieces of exoskeleton, so they may look at first glance as if they don't have these components.

Insects also have compound eyes and antennae. They have a multi-staged development of either complete or partial metamorphosis – don't worry about those terms, I explain more on that on p.xiii. Finally, insects have a soundwave-detecting appendage called a Johnston's organ (*see* p.43), located in their antennae. Most of these aspects are characteristic of all insects, though there are some interesting rule breakers.

LIFE STAGES

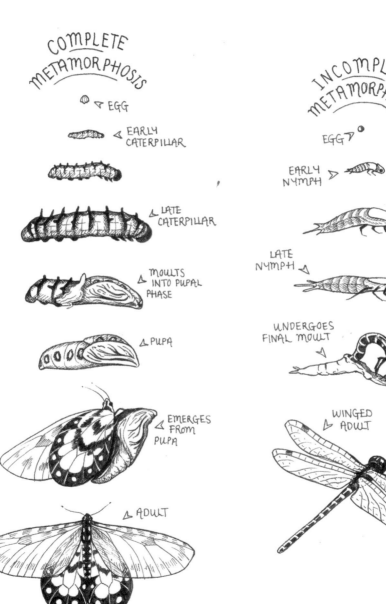

COMPLETE METAMORPHOSIS

◁ EGG

◁ EARLY CATERPILLAR

◁ LATE CATERPILLAR

◁ MOULTS INTO PUPAL PHASE

◁ PUPA

◁ EMERGES FROM PUPA

◁ ADULT

INCOMPLETE METAMORPHOSIS

EGG ▷

EARLY NYMPH ▷

LATE NYMPH ◁

UNDERGOES FINAL MOULT ▽

WINGED ◁ ADULT

HOW DO INSECTS DEVELOP?

Just like humans have an infancy, an adolescence and an adulthood, insects go through a few stages, though these can vary depending on the group.

Some insects go through large morphological changes from baby to adult, called complete metamorphosis (also known as holometabolous growth). *Complete metamorphosis* has four life stages: egg (lain by adult), larva (young, grub-like, and focused on feeding and growing), pupa (occurs when larvae develops into an immobile stage where internal reorganisation occurs), and adult (the fully developed adult insect emerges, bustin' out of that pupa like Marlon Brando out of his shirt in the 1951 film *A Streetcar Named Desire*). This four-stage development occurs in many insects that come to mind, such as butterflies, moths, beetles, bees, flies and ants.

Other insects go through *incomplete metamorphosis* (also known as hemimetabolous growth). This is where only three main life stages occur: egg (lain by adult), larva or nymph (usually these young insects look like smaller, wingless versions of the adults), adult (the growing insect moults a final time to reach their final, winged stage of adulthood). This final stage is typified by cicadas, who leave their delicate moulted skins on tree-trunks and grasses for us to discover.

TAXONOMY

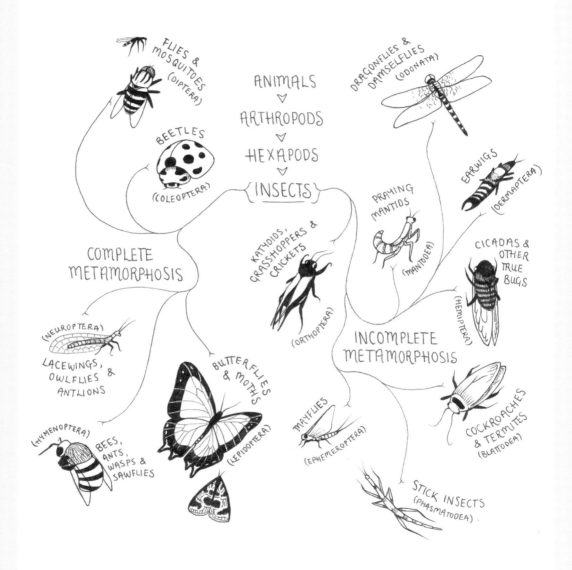

ANIMALS
▽
ARTHROPODS
▽
HEXAPODS
▽
{ INSECTS }

FLIES & MOSQUITOES (DIPTERA)

BEETLES (COLEOPTERA)

DRAGONFLIES & DAMSELFLIES (ODONATA)

EARWIGS (DERMAPTERA)

PRAYING MANTIDS (MANTODEA)

CICADAS & OTHER TRUE BUGS (HEMIPTERA)

COMPLETE METAMORPHOSIS

KATYDIDS, GRASSHOPPERS & CRICKETS (ORTHOPTERA)

(NEUROPTERA) LACEWINGS, OWLFLIES & ANTLIONS

BUTTERFLIES & MOTHS (LEPIDOPTERA)

INCOMPLETE METAMORPHOSIS

(HYMENOPTERA) BEES, ANTS, WASPS & SAWFLIES

MAYFLIES (EPHEMEROPTERA)

COCKROACHES & TERMITES (BLATTODEA)

STICK INSECTS (PHASMATODEA)

HOW TO USE THIS BOOK

PRACTICAL INFO FOR BUDDING ENTOMOLOGISTS

Welcome, beetle spotters and butterfly watchers, to the world of insects. This field guide is an on-ramp to help you understand Australia's insect life. View it as a tool kit – each species' entry will give you some information on the appearance, habitat and behaviours of an insect, which will help inform your broader understanding of insects in general.

This book is roughly split into four main sections: 'butterflies' (Lepidoptera, or butterflies and moths), 'bees' (Hymenoptera, or bees, ants and wasps), 'beetles' (Coleoptera), and finally 'insects', which is a mixed bag of true bugs, grasshoppers, dragonflies, mayflies, phasmids (stick and leaf insects), mantids, and a few other obscure species.

My goal is to provide you with a cross-section of the major groups of Australian insects, whilst also presenting species that have both an interesting life history, or have ecological and social significance. That said, this is simply an introductory 100 species, and I hope they kindle your curiosity to investigate further in scientific field guides as your confidence grows. Some detailed scientific field guides are listed in the bibliography (*see* p.203).

To get the most out of this guide, and your insect-watching ventures, it's worth understanding how different species of insects are related, and how closely they sit on a taxonomic tree. The diagram opposite will introduce you to the different taxonomic groups featured in this book. The scientific name bracketed underneath each insect type (e.g. 'Lepidoptera') is the name of the order, which is sort of like a family name. Learning to recognise different insect types can help you spot when species are closely related, due to their similar appearance or behaviours.

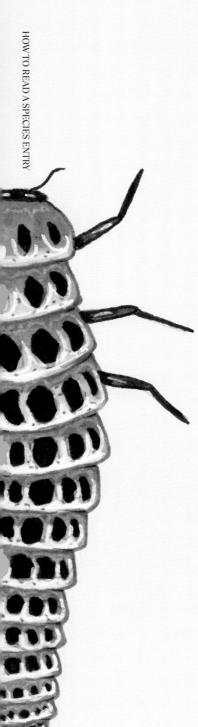

HOW TO READ A SPECIES ENTRY

❶ COMMON ENGLISH NAME e.g. Washerwoman Christmas beetle

(In some cases, where groups were too diverse to narrow down to just one species, I have entered the common name of the group, as in the case of jewel beetles, *see* p.103, or rove beetles, *see* p.115).

❷ FIRST PEOPLE'S NAMES AND PRONUNCIATION GUIDE e.g. Yugambeh language: *beengin* (BEEN-GIN), ('beetle').

First Nations Peoples of Australia have many specific names for insect species. Words in Alyawarr, Gumbaynggirr, Warlpiri and Yugambeh languages have been included with permission in relevant entries. The names displayed represent only a small diversity of First Nations terminology. I have included only some specific names for certain species, such as witchetty grubs (*see* p.53), whilst in other cases broader terms have been used for insect groups. For example, in Gumbaynggirr language, baarany refers to a moth or butterfly without specifying which species is being referred to.

Generous providers of language translations for this book are listed in the Acknowledgements (*see* pp.206–207).

❸ SCIENTIFIC NAME e.g. *Anoplognathus porusus*

This is the Latin binomial, or scientific name for the species (or the family, in cases where more than one species is featured). For the washerwoman Christmas beetle, the scientific name is *Anoplognathus porosus*. The first word, *Anoplognathus*, is the genus name. Imagine this as your surname – the name your siblings share with you. Other species with the genus name *Anoplognathus* will likely be similar in appearance and habits, rather like a family resemblance. This can be helpful when you are trying to ID species, because noticing similarities may lead you to a family or genus name. The second word, *porosus*, is the species name, and indicates the precise species – imagine this as your first name, unique to you. Sometimes, as in the case of the Eltham copper butterfly (*see* p.19), a subspecies is also provided. Subspecies are identified when a single species contains so much variation it is considered to have multiple subspecies. Don't let these

❸
Anoplognathus
porosus

❷
ALYAWARR LANGUAGE
ident ident: pronounced ai-KINT-al-kint',
'small white grub', *Anoplognathus olivieri*,
species Christmas beetle larva, lit. 'moon
moon'.

YUGAMBEH LANGUAGE
tengin BEEN-GIN', 'beetle'.

WARLPIRI LANGUAGE
mir MIH-jee', 'scarab beetle', 'Christmas
beetle'.

❹

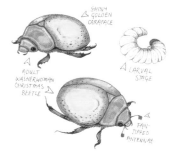

SHINY
GOLDEN
CARAPACE

ADULT
WASHERWOMAN
CHRISTMAS
BEETLE

LARVAL
STAGE

FAN-
TIPPED
ANTENNAE

❶ WASHERWOMAN CHRISTMAS BEETLE

❺ Though associated by name with Christmas traditions, these gloriously shiny beetles have always been a symbol of both seasonal and annual change, regardless of what end-of-year ritual was happening. As a kid, I would often gently lift green, copper and gold Christmas beetles off the ledge outside the kitchen window, where they gathered thickly at night, drawn towards the light. When you had one on your hand you could look closely at their amazing colour, and their spectacular, armoured anatomy. I think for many people growing up in Australia, when the Christmas beetles started gathering on the verandah light, you knew that summer had arrived. Perhaps one of the most readily recognised of the Christmas beetles is the washerwoman Christmas beetle. A common visitor to gardens, verandahs, flyscreens, kitchens, lawns and trees, these golden beetles arrive in the hot summer months and feed on eucalypt leaves, flying clumsily and briefly between destinations.

In earlier decades, Christmas beetles, the washerwoman included, were considered significant pests due to their high consumption of leaves, sometimes defoliating plantation trees. However, most likely due to habitat loss, Christmas beetles have become a rarer sight. I have referred to *A. porosus* as the 'washerwoman Christmas beetle' but, due to a fair bit of pattern and colour variation, *Anoplognathus* species beetles are readily confused for one another, and thus often have multiple – or shared – common names.

WHAT TO LOOK FOR A big, shiny, golden beetle, about 20mm long. They have tiny branched antennae, like minute deer antlers (adorable). The larvae are white, horseshoe-shaped grubs that hang out in the soil.

LIFE CYCLE Adult female Christmas beetles lay eggs in the soil. The larvae wriggle their way to nearby root masses to feed on them. They pupate under the soil, then emerge as shining adult beetles, often crawling dazedly across grass lawns for a while before taking flight.

WHERE TO LOOK The washerwoman Christmas beetle can be seen along Australia's east coast, excluding Tasmania. They rely on eucalypt trees as adults, and usually are more numerous after a season of decent rain, though their

populations seem to fluctuate a lot year to year. The adult beetles are drawn to lights, so they may congregate around your house on summer nights. Some of my best Christmas beetle encounters have, strangely enough, been when visiting communal buildings at parks or in campgrounds, and seeing a huge array of beetles and other insects drawn to the fluorescent light.

WHEN TO LOOK Late spring and summer.

SIMILAR SPECIES There are about 35 species of Christmas beetles in Australia, mostly within the *Anoplognathus* genus. Most are an orange, gold, yellow or green colour with similar body shapes. One cute example is the granny smith beetle (*Anoplognathus prasinus*), found along the southern Queensland and NSW coast.

categories worry you too much – they are simply a frame through which you can recognise similarities and differences between insects. They can also help you to be accurate, as sometimes a single species may have many common names, making things confusing. A scientific name helps clarify exactly which insect you're describing.

It should be noted, new species and subspecies of insects are being described all the time, and so the taxonomy as recorded in this book will probably shift in the near future. Such is the still-blossoming nature of insect study.

❹ **MAP** Each map has a shaded section, which indicates where a species may be seen. In this example, the washerwoman Christmas beetle is likely to be seen along the east coast of Australia, excluding Tasmania, and unlikely to be seen across the rest of the continent.

⑤ INSECT ENTRY Each insect has an anecdotal description that covers some life habits, and other aspects of the insect that make them unique, as well as some personal observations.

Then there are several more specific sub-headings:

WHAT TO LOOK FOR This paints a picture of what the species looks like.

LIFE CYCLE This describes whether the insect goes through three or four stages in its development, and includes information about reproduction.

WHERE TO LOOK This tells you about which Australian regions and habitats the insect is found in, e.g. wetlands or rainforests. In some entries, I use general terms, such as alpine areas, and in others I specify a plant or particular environmental niche where the insect is likely to gather.

WHEN TO LOOK This tells you what time of year to look for the adults of a species.

HABITAT HELP This provides suggestions for how you can help the species, such as gardening tips, how you can support an insect in your local area, and information about conservation. Many thanks go to Laura Mumaw and Luis Mata for compiling and making available insect conservation information on behalf of Gardens for Wildlife Victoria (*see* p.204).

SIMILAR SPECIES This helps you identify some similar-looking species that might be mistaken for the featured species. In a few of the entries, I have included comparative illustrations to help you distinguish them.

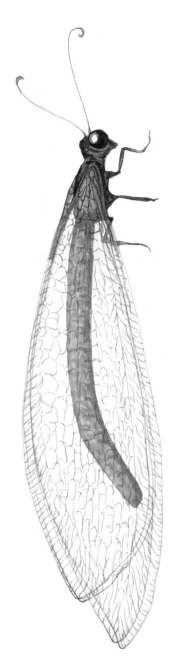

SOME QUESTIONS

There's a lot to learn about how insects have adapted.

HOW DO INSECTS BREATHE? Insects don't have lungs like mammals. Instead, they breathe through holes in their abdomen called spiracles. The movement of the abdomen means oxygen and carbon dioxide are exchanged into the circulatory system (a form of blood, called haemolymph) without needing lungs to pump air.

PUPA VS CHRYSALIS VS COCOON? A pupa, or chrysalis, is the immobile stage of development between larva and adult insect. It's most famed in butterflies, who go from being a caterpillar to an ovalish-shaped pupa, which eventually splits to free an adult butterfly. As for cocoons, not all insects that pupate necessarily have a cocoon. Many moths are known to spin cocoons, usually out of silk and debris, inside of which the pupa remains protected while developing.

INSTARS VS IMAGO? Instars are stages of larval development between moults. Imagine this as Anakin Skywalker's growth stages through adolescence, moving from a podracing kid into an apprentice Jedi teen. Imago is the last, winged, sexually active adult stage of an insect. If instars are young Anakin Skywalker, the imago is Darth Vader.

OVIPOSITOR? An ovipositor is an appendage that almost all female insects have at the tip of their abdomen. It is used for laying eggs, and is often specialised to allow an insect to lay eggs in a particular way. In most butterflies, the ovipositor is used to place eggs on leaves or plant stems. Female parasitic wasps, like the orchid dupe wasp (*see* p.63), have a needle-like ovipositor that is used to pierce other insects. In sawflies, females have a tiny saw-like appendage attached to their butt – I'm not joking – which they use to saw into plant stems and lay their eggs. Laying eggs is often termed ovipositing.

REPRODUCTION? OOTHECA? EGG? SPERMATOPHORE? WHAT? Insect sex is wild and pretty variable. Sometimes mating occurs on the wing, as with mosquitoes, while dragonflies often perch in elaborate poses for lengthy periods. In some insects, males deliver a package known as a spermatophore, which is both sperm to fertilise a female's eggs and also a nutritionally dense nugget of protein to improve her egg quality. In mantids, under-nourished females often consume their beau post or during coitus. Insects rarely rear their own young but they need a way to ensure their young remain (relatively) safe until they hatch. In some cases, individual eggs are lain in nooks or crannies or under leaves, as many butterflies do. In other cases, a female produces an ootheca (egg case) that contains multiple eggs.

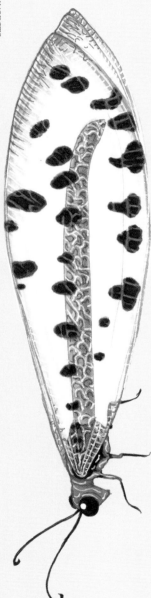

HOW TO ID INSECTS

There are so many insects that trying to identify a species can be daunting. Trust me, you'll learn quickly, and soon when someone sends you a picture of an obscure insect, you'll have the knowledge to at least identify the order, family or genus for them.

Usually, the first step is to look at the overall body shape of the insect. Is it round and shiny? (probably a beetle). Or small with wings? (probably a fly, bee, termite or perhaps a winged ant). Or does it have large colourful wings? (likely a butterfly or day-flying moth). Or maybe it has a long body with transparent wings (probably a dragonfly, damselfly, mayfly or lacewing). Usually then you can start to use distinguishing features (perhaps colour, appendages, patterning, or a particular behaviour) to help try and narrow to a family group, or genus or species.

The location or geographical distribution of the insect is also helpful in narrowing down which species it may be, as many insects are only found in certain parts of the country or in certain habitats.

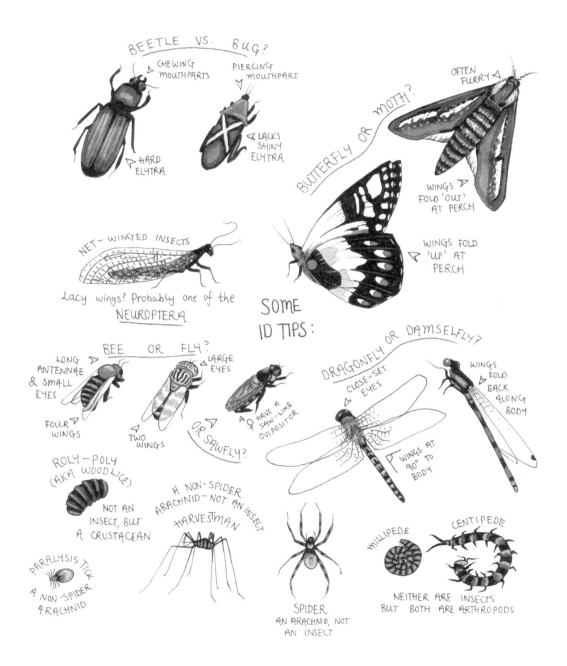

BEETLE VS. BUG?

CHEWING MOUTHPARTS

HARD ELYTRA

PIERCING MOUTHPART

LACKS SHINY ELYTRA

BUTTERFLY OR MOTH?

OFTEN FURRY

WINGS FOLD 'OUT' AT PERCH

WINGS FOLD 'UP' AT PERCH

NET-WINGED INSECTS

Lacy wings? Probably one of the NEUROPTERA

SOME ID TIPS:

BEE OR FLY?

LONG ANTENNAE & SMALL EYES

LARGE EYES

FOUR WINGS

TWO WINGS

OR SAWFLY?

♀ HAVE A SAW-LIKE OVIPOSITOR

DRAGONFLY OR DAMSELFLY?

CLOSE-SET EYES

WINGS FOLD BACK ALONG BODY

WINGS AT 90° TO BODY

ROLY-POLY (AKA WOODLICE)

NOT AN INSECT, BUT A CRUSTACEAN

A NON-SPIDER ARACHNID - NOT AN INSECT

HARVESTMAN

PARALYSIS TICK

A NON-SPIDER ARACHNID

SPIDER
AN ARACHNID, NOT AN INSECT

MILLIPEDE

CENTIPEDE

NEITHER ARE INSECTS BUT BOTH ARE ARTHROPODS

xxi

HOW, WHERE AND WHEN TO LOOK FOR INSECTS

HOW Conveniently, insects are everywhere. Inconveniently, insects are mostly tiny. So to breach that divide, it requires a little patience and curiosity to see and appreciate bugs. If you find yourself out on a walk, at a picnic, having a breath of fresh air on your work break, or in the garden, try standing still for a few moments. This will allow you to notice any movement at ground level or on nearby plants, and help you hone in on any insects. Often you may already be subconsciously aware of some movement, such as flies or bees buzzing around vegetation. Let yourself actually pause and inspect those little creatures, and observe how they might play into the systems of our environment. Taking a photograph, where possible, is immensely helpful, so you can compare species in detail without rushing.

WHERE The benefit of insects being tiny is they generally don't need too much space, so they can often be seen without having to travel much. One of the ultimate – and super accessible – ways to watch insects, is to spend time watching a flowering plant, ideally one with open flowers. It's easy to find insects in both native and non-native gardens, heathlands in spring, coastal banksia forests, or along roadsides where wild carrots/fennel/daisies flower (be careful of traffic, make sure you're in a safe place for getting distracted!). One other place I've been really successful in seeing a lot of strange insects is along ocean shores. I remember one evening at Wilson's Promontory, Wamoon/Yiruk, when a quick beachcomb uncovered jewel beetles, cicadas, native and European bees, Christmas beetles and feather-horned beetles. You can also try to look for insects at night, such as under fluorescent lights in camp kitchens or near streetlamps. Lighting up a white sheet outside can draw in a lot of interesting nocturnal species for you to get a closer look.

WHEN As cold-blooded animals, insects are much more active and abundant in spring and summer. You'll notice quickly, especially if you live in the southern half of Australia, that not only flowers herald the arrival of spring, but also thousands of different insect species. If you live in the more northern climes of Australia, you'll find there is more consistent insect activity year-round, due to prolonged warmth and rainfall. That said, there is a lot of local variation and, of course, there are some insect species that defy expectations and emerge in autumn, like the Key's matchstick grasshopper (*see* p.181). It should be noted that many species of insects enjoy only a very brief period of life as an adult, so sometimes it really is a matter of lucky timing. All the more reason to savour those encounters when they occur.

ETHICAL AND SAFE BUG-WATCHING

LOOKING AFTER INSECTS WHILE YOU LOOK AT THEM

While it's very important to learn about and appreciate the diverse insects of Australia, we should leave natural spaces as close to how we found them as possible, and insects, however numerous they may seem, should be left unharmed.

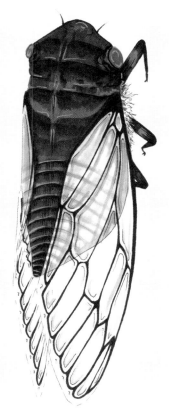

Turning over rotten logs to look for bess beetles, for example, is well and good, but we also have to be aware of what environment we are disturbing and how we may be impacting other creatures (snakes, spiders, antechinus and other native marsupials, skinks, etc.).

With this prospect under consideration, insects found in the home or garden can be treated gently. Most insects, if encroaching on your level of comfort, can readily be removed to a better place by trapping them under a glass, sliding a piece of cardboard underneath, and carrying them outside. In the garden, many native insects, like the common spotted ladybird (*see* p.101), rove beetles (*see* p.115) and hoverflies (*see* p.157) will actively feed on pest species, such as aphids and scale insects. As such, I would urge you to avoid use of pesticides on your garden. Most garden pesticides are broad-spectrum, meaning they kill not only pest species, but also beneficial natives as well.

Part-and-parcel with treating insects gently is the knowledge that many insects have defensive measures to try to keep predators at bay. Many of the hairy caterpillars (*see* pp.35–38) have painful, stinging hairs covering their bodies that can cause a nasty reaction in humans. Others, such as the jumping jack ant (*see* p.69), or wasps (*see* pp.61–65), have stings they will readily use to defend themselves. In most cases, it is much better to look and not touch.

SUPPORTING INSECT DIVERSITY

An invaluable resource for understanding how we can support insect diversity is a 2021 report, *Socio-ecological benefits of wildlife gardening*, written by Laura Mumaw and Luis Mata (*see* p.204). This report, based on research funded by Gardens for Wildlife Victoria, summarises the benefits – to both insects *and* humans – of creating invertebrate-friendly spaces in urban and suburban areas. Not only are insects, especially native insects, essential to ecosystem function, by equal measure caring for natural spaces and fostering biodiversity is essential for human health, at both an individual and community level. With the guidance of this report, and ecological information provided in scientific journals, I have made suggestions in certain entries on how you can provide support to that species. There are also general approaches to fostering insect life in your area which you can apply.

Try prioritising native plant species, which provide both food and habitat resources. This includes removing weeds, and protecting established native vegetation where it already occurs. Adding groundcover, tussock grasses, shrubs and canopy, if you have the space to do so, is also a way to support diverse native insect life. One way to consider contributing is growing just a handful of native plant species, which allows your balcony or garden to be a corridor for wildlife to flow through as they move between locations. Undisturbed nooks and crannies, decomposing wood and water features also create habitat spaces for insects to flourish within.

The fragmentation of habitat caused by urbanisation and agricultural practice is one of the largest catalysts of biodiversity loss, so even small contributions we make to protect and restore native habitat can make an enormous difference. Many people live within walking distance or can get public transport to a bushland reserve or park. Bush reserves, parklands and windbreaks, even in the middle of the CBD, can be considered ecological islands in which native species can take refuge. For example, Key's matchstick grasshopper (*see* p.181) was found sheltering amongst unmown native grasses in cemeteries.

CITIZEN SCIENCE AND INSECT-WATCHING

Citizen science, in the context of ecology, is pretty straightforward: it's sharing observations of natural phenomena to contribute to our collective understanding. These observations come from citizens, whether well-read scientists, amateur naturalists, or people completely new to looking at the natural world. Sharing observations usually comprises taking a photo, or even simply recording a sighting, usually through a free app or a website, such as the Atlas of Living Australia or iNaturalist. These applications pool data from across the country, creating an online record with enormous detail about the habitat type, distribution, amount, behaviour and appearance of both native and introduced species in Australia.

The beauty of citizen science is that it gathers a breadth of data that couldn't be achieved with a small group of professional researchers. Just as it takes thousands of individual voters to elect a government, it takes a whole population of people making contributions to help us comprehend Australia's biodiversity. If you are able, download a citizen science app, or jump on to one of the websites, and try logging one of your recent sightings.

A NOTE ABOUT THIS BOOK

Information for this book was compiled from research papers, citizen observations, personal communication with entomologists, and many excellent field guides, which are listed in the bibliography (*see* p.203).

This guide is intended to give an introduction to Australia's native insects, and while I've made every effort to ensure the information is accurate at the time of printing, it is likely – even hopeful – that some of the information in this volume will be further clarified in the future, or even become outdated. Insects are often effective dispersers, so geographical distributions will change, as will seasonal behaviours due to climate change. In entries, I have suggested the likely times of year to see adults of a species. However, if there is a year of unseasonably wet weather, or a long period of drought, insect patterns will, of course, differ. In addition to behavioural and distribution information, taxonomy will also change as our understanding of evolutionary links between species expands. It is likely that the classifications of species as they are listed in this book will change in coming years.

I have illustrated species throughout this book with attention to detail, but they are still shown through my own artistic lens – you may find insects in your explorations that vary in appearance from my drawings.

So, while I've made efforts to be accurate, information will be expanded by dedicated entomologists in the coming years. Keep recording your own observations, be a citizen scientist (*see* p.xxv), and we can all contribute to a greater understanding of Australian insects.

Graphium macleayanum

GUMBAYNGGIRR LANGUAGE
baarany (pronounced BAA-rany), ('moth' or 'butterfly').

YUGAMBEH LANGUAGE
banjalahm (BUN-ja-LAHM), ('butterfly').

MACLEAY'S
SWALLOWTAIL

'SWALLOWTAIL'
TIPPED
HIND-
WINGS

FOURBAR
SWORDTAIL

NOTE
LENGTHENED
HINDWING
TIPS

MACLEAY'S SWALLOWTAIL
CATERPILLAR

MACLEAY'S SWALLOWTAIL BUTTERFLY

One particularly busybody species of butterfly I often see in the High Country is the Macleay's swallowtail. They are visibly different from many other butterflies in the area – they are big, strikingly coloured green and black, and they have elongated hindwing tips. They further draw attention by furiously chasing off other butterflies, despite being enormously outnumbered. We think of butterflies as delicate and gentle creatures, but in reality some of them are fierce and will fight and batter themselves to assert dominance. The Macleay's swallowtail is vehemently territorial, tirelessly chasing off encroaching butterflies without pausing to feed from the flowers that make up much of their heathland habitat.

One memorable day, I climbed Mount Mackay above Falls Creek in Victoria (Jaitmatang Country) and watched one very grumpy Macleay's swallowtail chase off cabbage white butterflies for almost an hour. It sounds absurd but it was riveting stuff! Like some other butterflies, Macleay's swallowtails tend to 'hilltop', a term that describes the congregation of adult butterflies at the highest visible point, such as at the top of a hill or a telephone pole. Here, they essentially flex to try to seduce nearby mates. Despite their slightly angry, chaotic energy, these butterflies are beautiful, and are determined, agile fliers, standing out vividly amongst the heathlands.

WHAT TO LOOK FOR Macleay's swallowtail butterflies have a wingspan of about 55mm, and are lime-green with black patterning. Each hindwing has an elongated tip, hence the name 'swallowtail' (swallows – the birds – have a long, forked tail, visible when they fly overhead). The caterpillars, when mature, are green with faint white stripes over their back.

LIFE CYCLE Adult Macleay's swallowtail butterflies lay their eggs on a variety of plants – often sassafras, camphor laurel and citrus – on which the caterpillars feed after hatching. The subspecies for Tasmania is known as *G. macleayanum moggana*, and as a caterpillar exclusively feeds on one food plant – southern sassafras. The caterpillar grows to about 40mm in length and then produces a green pupa on the underside of a leaf. After pupating, the adult butterfly emerges.

WHERE TO LOOK Along the east coast from around Cairns in Queensland, south to Melbourne/Naarm and in Tasmania. They are the only swallowtail species recorded in Tasmania, which makes them a particularly unique species to see there. On the mainland, I've often seen Macleay's swallowtail butterflies in heathlands or flower-rich bushland areas of the alpine country.

WHEN TO LOOK Spring through to early autumn in the south, depending on seasonal variation. Further up the coast, they can be seen year-round.

HABITAT HELP Encouraging flowering natives in your garden and protecting bush reserves can support butterflies and increase your chance of seeing them. In Tasmania, growing or protecting southern sassafras is a good way to ensure that this swallowtail species survives.

SIMILAR SPECIES Pale green triangle (*Graphium eurypylus*) found in coastal NSW, Queensland, NT and WA), Fourbar swordtail (*Protographium leosthenes*, pictured opposite) seen in north-east NSW, along the Queensland coast, and a small area of the NT).

Ornithoptera euphorion

CATERPILLAR

♀

PUPA

FEMALES ARE
BLACK, WHITE &
YELLOW

♂

MALES ARE
VIBRANT GREEN
& BLACK

DISTINCTIVE
MALE UNDER-
WING
PATTERNS

CAIRNS BIRDWING BUTTERFLY

Though restricted to a narrow area of the Queensland coast, the Cairns birdwing is a readily recognised and beloved species of Australian butterfly. These enormous insects are strikingly patterned in black, green and yellow hues, and, at their largest size can have a wingspan of about 15cm, hence these creatures make for an amazing sight. Their wings are so big they flex much like feathered bird wings, rather than the delicate scaled membranes they actually are.

After mating, male Cairns birdwings often guard the female butterfly to prevent other males from copulating with her. Impressively, when visiting suburban gardens, these butterflies have been seen scaring off small nectar feeding birds, allowing the butterflies to keep these sugary blossoms to themselves. Muhammad Ali recommended floating like a butterfly, and stinging like a bee, but I think you could throw a pretty good haymaker punch if you were a Cairns birdwing.

WHAT TO LOOK FOR Female and male Cairns birdwings are sexually dimorphic, meaning the male and female butterflies look different from one another. The males are about 120mm in wingspan, with brilliant green hindwings, and black and green forewings. Females are larger, sometimes up to 150mm in wingspan, largely black, with yellow patterning on the hindwing, and white patterning on the forewing. The caterpillars are black with two yellow-white spikes on the central portion of the body. Like other swallowtail butterflies (*see* p.1), Cairns birdwing caterpillars can produce a forked orange appendage called an osmoterium (a bit like a tentacle). The caterpillar can display this to scare-off would-be predators.

LIFE CYCLE Females lay eggs on native birthwort plants (*Aristolochia*). It should be noted there is a species of introduced birthwort that is poisonous to Cairns birdwings: the South American vine *Aristolochia elegans*. After hatching, the caterpillars feed until they are about 60mm long, then pupate on the underside of a nearby leaf. These clever caterpillars actually build a little 'guy rope' around their waist (known as a girdle), which

supports their pupa while they industriously metamorphose out of sight. After pupating, a magnificent adult butterfly emerges.

WHERE TO LOOK These beautiful butterflies are residents of the tropical mountainous areas of northern Queensland. If you're in that area, look for them in gardens, parks or bush reserves.

WHEN TO LOOK Year-round. Depending on seasonal conditions, these butterflies can produce several generations of adults within a year.

HABITAT HELP Planting native birthwort species, *Aristolochia acuminata* or *Pararistolochia deltantha*, provides these butterflies with food plants. The removal of non-native *Aristolochia* vines is also a good way to support this species.

SIMILAR SPECIES The New Guinea birdwing (*Ornithoptera priamus*, found in Cape York in Queensland) and the orchard swallowtail (*Papilio aegeus*, found across Victoria, and along eastern NSW and Queensland) both look similar to the Cairns birdwing butterfly.

Cressida cressida

ALYAWARR LANGUAGE
ntelyapelyap (pronounced (i)n-dil-YAP-il-yap)
('butterfly' or 'moth').

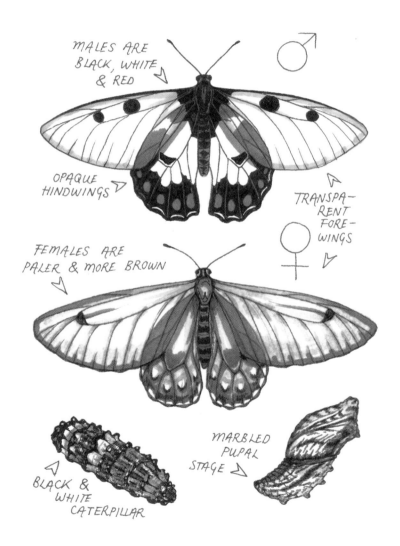

MALES ARE
BLACK, WHITE
& RED ▷

♂

OPAQUE
HINDWINGS ▷

TRANSPA-
RENT
FORE-
WINGS ◁

♀

FEMALES ARE
PALER & MORE BROWN
▽

BLACK &
WHITE
CATERPILLAR
△

MARBLED
PUPAL
STAGE ▷

BIG GREASY BUTTERFLY

Adult big greasy butterflies have transparent wings, which is a surreal phenomena amongst butterflies. The females are much like the males, only paler and more sepia coloured, almost like a ghostly apparition dancing alongside their full-colour male counterparts. As a member of the swallowtail family (Papillionidae), the big greasy butterfly is also known as a clearwing swallowtail.

One of the most notable – and slightly disturbing – habits of the big greasy butterfly is their mating ritual. When a male big greasy pursues a female to mate, the male transfers his sperm in a hardened plug (known as a sphragis), which essentially plugs the female genitalia and prevents her from mating with any other male. In terms of a genetic scurry, this approach definitely goes by the first-in, best-dressed approach. The female, having mated once, then gets about her life with this sphragis poking from her abdomen, obliged into a life of sexual abstinence. Several other species of butterfly have a 'sexual plug' that similarly stops a female butterfly from mating a second time, but in the case of the big greasy, the plug is particularly conspicuous. The sphragis can be so large it can be seen with the naked eye, encumbering the female while she tries to clamber over flowers. What a hassle.

WHAT TO LOOK FOR A large black, red and white butterfly, with transparent forewings. The wingspan is approximately 70mm, though they're known for size variation. Males have forewings with two black spots, and hindwings patterned with white, black and red. Females have transparent forewings *and* hindwings, both of which have a sepia tinge. The caterpillars are brown-black with white spots, covered in little spikes (at first glance, they could be mistaken for bird droppings).

LIFE CYCLE Big greasy caterpillars have a proclivity for birthwort plants (*Aristolochia* spp.), hence adults tend to lay eggs on these vines. The caterpillars hatch and feed until ready to pupate. Perching on a branch or stem, they shed into their pupal form, producing an amazing brown and white marbled pupa, which props on branches or stems, supported by a little girdle. When ready, an adult big greasy butterfly emerges.

WHERE TO LOOK Along the north coast of Australia, with a range extending to the NSW/Queensland border on the east coast, with the occasional trail-blazing big greasy making it as far south as Gumbaynggirr Country (Coffs Harbour region). Look in bushland reserves and gardens in the north, especially where birthwort vines grow.

WHEN TO LOOK Warmer months in the south of its range, year-round in the north.

HABITAT HELP Planting native birthwort vine species (*Aristolochia acuminata* or *Pararistolochia deltantha)*, and removing invasive *Aristolochia* vines can support this species.

SIMILAR SPECIES The dingy swallowtail (*Papilio anactus*), is found along the east coast to Melbourne/Naarm. Although a member of a different family of butterflies (Nymphalidae), the gorgeous glasswing butterfly is (adorably) known as the 'little greasy' (*Acraea andromacha, see* p.xiv.) and is found across the northern half of Australia.

Graphium sarpedon

COMMON
BLUEBOTTLE

WELL
CAMOUFLAGED
PUPAL
STAGE

BLUE
TRIANGLE
SYMBOL
ACROSS
WINGS

COMMON
BLUEBOTTLE
CATERPILLAR

ULYSSES
SWALLOWTAIL

COMMON BLUEBOTTLE BUTTERFLY

Like the Macleay's swallowtail (*see* p.1), common bluebottle butterflies are *busy*, restlessly scooting about and chasing away other butterflies. When they do land to sip nectar or water, it's often a brief, fluttering pause before they resume their erratic flight. With patience, hopefully you'll be able to watch one when it finally decides to pause for a few moments, allowing you to properly admire its magnificent wings. It is a special sight to see these butterflies gathered at the edges of puddles where they pause to drink.

This butterfly is part of the Swallowtail family (Papilionidae), although the common bluebottle's hindwings are not as lengthy as some other swallowtail species. When seen from behind, the patterning on the common bluebottle's open wings form a point-down triangle, hence the other common name for this species: the blue triangle butterfly.

WHAT TO LOOK FOR A large blue and black coloured butterfly, with a wingspan of about 55mm. The underside of the hindwings have some hard-to-spot red patterns. The caterpillars are green with short spikes towards the head. Like other swallowtail caterpillars (*see* p.1), they have a tentacle-like organ called an osmoterium that they can expose if threatened.

LIFE CYCLE Adult common bluebottle butterflies lay their eggs on food plants – often camphor laurel plants, though the caterpillars have a wide array of tastes. After feeding and growing to about 30mm long, the caterpillar forms a pupa, usually on the underside of a leaf. After a couple of weeks of warm weather, an adult common bluebottle butterfly emerges.

WHERE TO LOOK These butterflies habituate suburban gardens and bushland along the east coast, from Cape York down to just north of Ngunnawal Country (Canberra/Ngambri/Ngunnawal). They usually remain on the coastal side of mountain ranges and seem to prefer lusher areas of bushland or even rainforest areas. You could try looking in gardens or places where camphor laurel grows (sometimes along roadsides or park edges in urban areas). These butterflies associate with several different plant types, so any areas with good native plant diversity are also places where you might spot one of these fluttering, vivid-blue triangles.

WHEN TO LOOK Spring and summer in the south, year-round in the north.

SIMILAR SPECIES Ulysses swallowtail (*Papilio ulysses* pictured opposite), is found along the Queensland coast. The pale triangle (*Graphium eurypylus*), of similar size but paler in colour, is found along the north and east coast of Australia.

Delias aganippe

ALYAWARR LANGUAGE
akwelethakwel-ayerr (pronounced a-KOOL-it-a-KOOL-ay-erd-a), ('red grub that lives in mistletoe').

WARLPIRI LANGUAGE
jajutuma (JUDGE-oo-doom-a), ('caterpillar').

SPOTTED
JEZEBEL
CATERPILLAR

SPOTTED
JEZEBEL

COLOURS ON
UNDERSIDE OF
WINGS

IMPERIAL
JEZEBEL

WINGS
ARE
DARKER

SPOTTED JEZEBEL BUTTERFLY

One spring morning, I was delighted by the sight of a flowering eucalypt tree in my neighbours' yard, alive with colourful butterflies. These showy insects were spotted jezebels, which are large, striking butterflies that hungrily sip nectar from flowering plants, especially from sugar-rich gum tree blossoms. There are several related 'jezebel' butterflies in Australia, but the fast-flying spotted jezebel has to be one of the more beautifully patterned ones. Part of the family Pieridae (the 'whites and yellows'), the spotted jezebel is a lover of open bushland, earning them the alternate name 'wood white'. The upper side of their wings are indeed white, but the underside of their wings is where their spectacular red, yellow and black patterns are displayed.

These butterflies are fairly well-adapted to survive even in arid bushland areas, rather than remaining within the more lush forests and gardens that many butterfly species habituate. Their spread to inland areas is probably mirrored, like others in the jezebel genus (*Delias*), by their love for parasitic plants, usually sandalwood and mistletoe. Mistletoe is the food source that spotted jezebel caterpillars love best, so the adults tend to linger near these plants as well. Male spotted jezebels are often seen gathered at hilltops or other high points in the landscape. The caterpillars readily feed on the leaves of mistletoe, while adults dance about in their colourful outfits, like court jesters.

WHAT TO LOOK FOR A red, yellow, black and white butterfly, with a wingspan of about 60mm. The upperside of the wings are white with black patterning framing both wings. The underside of the forewing is also black and white, while the hindwing is patterned with red and yellow markings. The caterpillars are reddish-brown with white hairs.

LIFE CYCLE After mating, a female spotted jezebel generally lays eggs on the leaves or stem of a parasitic plant, such as mistletoe growing on an acacia tree. The caterpillars hatch and feed on the leaves of the mistletoe. When ready, the caterpillar usually retreats into the leaves of the host tree (in this case, the host acacia) to pupate, and later emerges as an adult butterfly.

WHERE TO LOOK South-west WA from Minang Country (Albany area) to Kariyarra Country (Port Hedland area), and in south-east SA, across Victoria and NSW, and sometimes in southern Queensland. Your best bet is to go to areas of established native bushland where mistletoe grows. Try looking in parklands, bush reserves or along watercourses, especially where native trees are flowering.

WHEN TO LOOK Year-round, excluding the coldest months of winter.

HABITAT HELP Looking after and preserving old-growth native bushland is essential to supporting jezebel species, as older trees are most likely to support diverse groups of mistletoe plants.

SIMILAR SPECIES Imperial jezebel (*Delia harpalyce* pictured opposite), seen across Victoria and eastern NSW; scarlet jezebel (*Delias argenthona*), found in northern and eastern Australia; caper white (*Belenois java*), lacking red patterns, and seen sparsely across all of Australia, excluding Tasmania and the south-west.

Euploea core

BLUE
TIGER

COMMON
CROW

WHITE DOTS
ALONG WING
MARGINS

COMMON
CROW
CATERPILLAR

COMMON CROW BUTTERFLY

Butterflies in the Crow genus, *Euploa*, are sometimes called 'milkweed butterflies'. This name comes from some sequestering habits the Crow butterflies perform using milkweed plants. Being a Crow butterfly is kind of like being on an episode of the reality show 'Hoarders', only these insects don't hoard objects – they hoard chemicals. Both the caterpillars and adult butterflies visit plants that are high in certain compounds – bitter-tasting chemicals, found in plants like daisies, borage, dogbane and oleander plants. These plants often ooze milky, acrid sap if broken, hence the name 'milkweed'. By consuming these plants, bitter chemicals build up in the body of the common crow butterfly, making them taste nasty to a range of predators, including birds and spiders.

Common crow butterflies that live in the northern areas of their range can enter a hibernation state to survive the winter months. During this time, they rely on tiny but essential fat reserves to make it through to the next breeding season, waiting for the next growth-spurt in vegetation to ensure any future larvae will be well fed. When entering this phase (the dry season from May to September-ish), they gather in huge numbers in secluded sections of bushland, where they remain for the cooler months of the year.

WHAT TO LOOK FOR A black butterfly with white dots along the wing edges, and a white-dotted body, with a wingspan of about 70mm. The caterpillars are orange with black and white stripes. They also have beautiful, curling black sensory tentacles paired along their body. The pupa starts out a creamy wax colour, but quickly hardens into a metallic surface that is so shiny it partially reflects its surroundings. Several other species of butterfly within this family, Nymphalidae, also have a metallic-coloured pupa.

LIFE CYCLE Female common crow butterflies tend to lay eggs one at a time on a large variety of introduced or native food plants. Larvae start feeding immediately upon hatching, munching for about a month, growing into lush orange-and-black caterpillars. A mature caterpillar then moults into its incredible gold pupa, from which an adult butterfly eventually emerges.

WHERE TO LOOK Along the north and east coastlines, occasionally seen as far south as Gunaikurnai Country (the Gippsland Lakes region in Victoria), usually in bushland, parks, gardens and tea tree scrub. When overwintering, these butterflies gather in gorges, gullies or along watercourses where they are buffered from the weather. Picture a gully in Queensland, where every bough and vine of the forest is carpeted with the black and white wings of the common crow.

WHEN TO LOOK Year-round in the north (though inactive over the dry season), or spring and summer in the southern areas of their range.

SIMILAR SPECIES Varied Eggfly (*see* p.15). Many other crow butterfly species look similar, such as the Eastern Brown Crow (*Euploea tulliolus*), found along the Queensland coast. The Blue Tiger Butterfly (*Tirumala hamata*), pictured opposite), also overwinters along the north and east coast.

Polyura sempronius

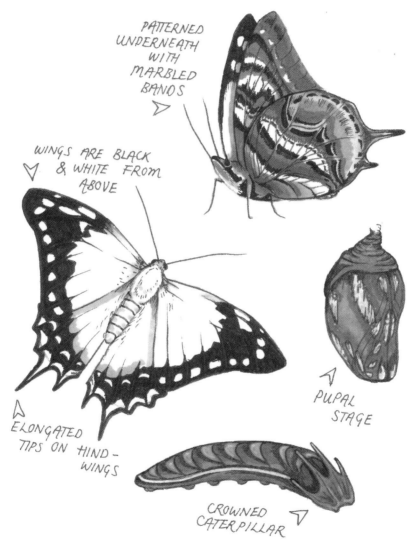

PATTERNED
UNDERNEATH
WITH
MARBLED
BANDS

WINGS ARE BLACK
& WHITE FROM
ABOVE

ELONGATED
TIPS ON HIND-
WINGS

PUPAL
STAGE

CROWNED
CATERPILLAR

TAILED EMPEROR BUTTERFLY

Like a vision out of an Ancient Greek myth, such as Poseidon or some other triton-wielding god, the tailed emperor butterfly is a sight to behold. The adult butterflies are distinctly black and white, with two 'prongs' at the tip of each hindwing, whilst the underside of the wings are patterned with marbled colours. The adult butterflies are known for their fierce territorial clashes between males when seeking a mate – often their wings are left tattered from these battles. They have also been observed feeding not only from flowers and sap flows from wounded trees, but also from the dung of native animals. Dung likely provides some obscure nutrients and minerals to these shrewd butterflies that are less readily available in nectar.

Whilst the resourceful and aggressive adults are already fascinating, the aspect of the tailed emperor that really takes the cake (for me) is the caterpillar, which has a set of 'horns' on its head, projected backwards like a regal crown. There is something so endearing about a tiny but hungry green caterpillar wearing a crown, munching away at leaves, as if it knew it was destined for glory post-metamorphosis.

WHAT TO LOOK FOR A white and black butterfly with two prongs on each hindwing, with a wingspan of around 90mm. The underside of the wings have marbled bands of white, brown and orange. The caterpillars are green with a set of yellow crescent moon-shaped bands across their back. They also have four tiny horns on their head.

LIFE CYCLE Adult tailed emperor butterflies often lay eggs on plants in the pea family (Fabaceae), but will lay on many other plant types too. After hatching, the caterpillar feeds on foliage, growing, until, when ready, it finds a stem from which to develop its pupa. After pupating, an adult tailed emperor emerges and heads off in search of food and a mate.

WHERE TO LOOK Along the north coast of WA and NT, from Cape York in Queensland through to Victoria, although it should noted their appearances in southern NSW and Victoria are infrequent. Adults feed from a wide array of flowers, but are also drawn to damaged fruits, sap flows from wounded trees and, occasionally, mammalian dung. Keep an eye out amongst bushland reserves, heathland and gardens.

WHEN TO LOOK Spring and summer in the southern areas of their range, year-round in the north.

SIMILAR SPECIES Though of a different butterfly family, Macleay's swallowtail looks similar (*see* p.1).

Hypolimnas bolina

PATTERNS VARY ◁

♀

PUPAL STAGE ▷

♂

VARIED EGGFLY CATERPILLAR

BLUE MOON PATTERNS

VARIED EGGFLY BUTTERFLY

Like a lot of other Australian butterfly species, the varied eggfly has many a confounding, similar-looking relative to confuse a budding entomologist. The adult females of this species add to this confusion by sometimes developing several different colours and patterns within the one generation. This phenomena is known as polymorphism, meaning 'many forms'.

The females vary greatly, some of them with sections of orange and brown, while others are largely black, with a white 'fringe' of dots down their wing edge. Some of these patterns appear to mimic nasty-tasting – and therefore well-defended – species of butterfly, such as the common crow butterfly (*see* p.11). This strategy is known as Batesian Mimicry. By assuming the appearance of something scary and/or toxic, the mimicking species appears to be dangerous, without having to put any actual effort in to accumulating poisonous chemicals in their systems. Batesian Mimicry is something of a 'fake it till you make it' style approach.

WHAT TO LOOK FOR These butterflies are dimorphic, so the males look quite different from the females. Males are black, with a big blue 'moon' on each hindwing, and two white dots towards the tip of each forewing. The females vary in appearance, so the males are the more reliable indicators of the species. That said, most females have dark wings, with white and orange patches on the forewing. Both males and females have a wingspan of about 65mm. The caterpillars are black, with orange spikes and an orange head.

LIFE CYCLE Females usually lay eggs sparsely on the undersides of leaves, on a range of both native and introduced plants. The larvae hatch, feed and grow until ready to pupate, after which an adult butterfly emerges.

WHERE TO LOOK The varied eggfly can be seen in northern WA, across NT and down the east coast, excluding Tasmania. They are more common in the wet forested areas of the coast, but venture into drier inland areas occasionally. Look for them in bushland reserves or parks. Flowers draw in adult butterflies, so you may spot some in suburban gardens.

WHEN TO LOOK Spring and summer in the south, year-round in the north, though less common during the dry season.

SIMILAR SPECIES Common crow (*see* p.11), Danaid eggfly (*Hypolimnas misippus*), Blue-banded eggfly (*Hypolimnas alimena*), both with a similar range to the varied eggfly.

Vanessa itea

YELLOW
ADMIRAL

YELLOW
ADMIRAL
CATERPILLAR

RED
LACE
WING

YELLOW ADMIRAL BUTTERFLY

Also known as the Australian admiral, these fast-flying butterflies are always a lovely sight. They have striking cream-coloured patches on their wings, which I think of as an admiral's epaulettes (those fancy shoulder decorations on a military uniform). Yellow admirals are a great species to try and spot, as they are common in both suburban and bushland areas, especially during the warmer months. Adult yellow admirals feed on nectar, but will also drink tree sap when it flows from damaged trunks or broken branches. I mean, any sugar is good sugar, right? Sometimes you'll get lucky and see a territorial yellow admiral male remain still for a time, displaying his wings from a visible, sunny perch to try to catch the attention of females. Most of the time, however, they are quite active and fast fliers.

I've spent plenty of time chasing these butterflies around with my phone, trying to snap pics, but they usually outwit me. On one such occasion, I was walking along a trail in the High Country, and I chased a yellow admiral from shrub to shrub, desperately trying to get a picture. Finally, I gave up and sat down to have a drink. Next minute, the bold little butterfly had the nerve to come and land on the very hand that was holding my phone. Touché, admiral, touché. Trust an ephemeral, tiny invertebrate to remind me that sometimes it's just better to absorb the moment.

WHAT TO LOOK FOR A striking rusty-brown and black butterfly, with a wingspan of about 50mm. These butterflies have both large and several smaller cream-coloured splotches leading into the tip of each forewing. The underwings are patterned with browns and greys, making them quite well camouflaged amongst leaf litter. There is also a blue eye-spot on the underside of each forewing. The caterpillars are grey-brown and spiky.

LIFE CYCLE Yellow admirals lay eggs most often on nettle family plants (Urticaceae), including stinging nettle, and the larvae feed on these soon after hatching. In an extremely cute manoeuvre, the young caterpillars will wrap themselves up using a nettle leaf, usually waiting for nightfall to re-emerge and feed again. The caterpillars feed until they are about 30mm long, then pupate on or near the nettle plants.

WHERE TO LOOK Across Victoria, eastern NSW and southern Queensland, and along the coast of south-east WA. Look in gardens, alpine and coastal heathlands, along creeks or lake edges. Near my home, they often feed in small groups from the flowering shrubs in people's front yards. It's also worth looking in areas where nettles are abundant.

WHEN TO LOOK Year-round, depending on seasonal conditions.

HABITAT HELP Although nettles, especially stinging nettles, are a nasty surprise in your garden, it can be worth leaving some dedicated patches where these weedy plants can grow and sustain local yellow admiral populations.

SIMILAR SPECIES Red lacewing (*Cethosia cydippe*, pictured opposite); Australian painted lady, found across Australia.

Paralucia pyrodiscus (subspecies *lucida*)

CLUBBED ANTENNAE

COPPER PANELS IN WINGS

GREY-BROWN UNDER WINGS

ATTENDANT *Notoncus* spp. ANTS

ELTHAM COPPER CATERPILLAR

ELTHAM COPPER BUTTERFLY

You might be surprised to learn how readily remnant patches of native bushland in urban settings can support endangered insects, as is the case of the Eltham copper butterfly. These insects are an endangered subspecies of the dull copper butterfly, a species found along the coast of NSW and in south-east Queensland. The Eltham copper is the only representative of the species found in central and western Victoria. These rare butterflies are members of the interesting butterfly family Lycaenidae, known as the 'blues'. Many of the 'blues' butterflies are a blue or copper colour, such as the common grass-blue (*see* p.20), the southern purple azure (*see* p.20), the copper ant blue, and the silky hairstreak (*see* p.23).

Perhaps contributing to their vulnerability, the Eltham copper has some very niche living requirements, like a pop star who requires certain expensive accoutrements in their dressing room. Like a little caterpillar-shaped diva, they need certain associated ant species to act as their bodyguard, plus they need a very particular diet of a plant called sweet bursaria. As peculiar as this may seem, the whole 'blues' family of butterflies containing the Eltham copper are particularly interesting, the majority of them associate with ants in one way or another. Where in many cases a soft, juicy caterpillar would be a prime food target for ants to feed to their brood, blues caterpillars have a few strategies to stop ants from eating them and, instead, encourage the ants to actually *protect* them. Some relationships between blues caterpillars and ants are symbiotic (to the benefit of both species), some are exploitative, and some are downright parasitic, such as the case of the moth butterfly and weaver ants (*see* p.67).

The caterpillars of blues butterflies exude a sugary substance from a special organ on their back as they feed. This secretion is a combination of sugars and amino acids from their diet of plant matter – both valuable resources to a hungry worker ant. The ants love to sip away at this secretion, and in turn provide the feeding caterpillars a measure of protection from predation, usually by their collective shepherding or gathering around the grub. The ants often crawl around and over the caterpillar while it feeds (picture a security detail for a celebrity). Despite the squishy caterpillar being largely defenseless, these ants instead opt to protect the source of their sugary addiction, instead of eating the grub and calling it a day. Some blues butterflies even pupate within an ant colony (the Eltham copper butterfly does this), or on the plant above or very nearby to their associated ant colony, as in the case of the silky hairstreak (*see* p.23).

Many of the blues butterflies have a reinforced cuticle (skin) that protects them from the initial curious proddings of ants. Some of them also are able to mimic certain chemical signals that both subdue aggressive ants, and coax them into defending the caterpillar as if it were a member of the ants' own brood. Blues butterflies are like little hypnotists, using chemical and sugar bribery to say: 'ants, it would be *much* better if, instead of carrying me back to your pantry, you defended me, and picnicked on my sugary exudes. This is the beginning of a beautiful friendship.'

SILVER
UNDER
WINGS ▷

COMMON
GRASS-BLUE ▷

SOUTHERN
PURPLE
AZURE

FIERY
JEWEL

◁ ATTENDANT
ANTS

SOUTHERN
PURPLE AZURE
CATERPILLAR

The Eltham copper subspecies only associates with a particular genus of ants (*Notoncus* ants, pictured opposite), who feed on the honeydew-esque secretions of the Eltham copper caterpillar. *Notoncus* ants build nests under sweet bursaria plants, limiting the regions in which the Eltham copper can survive. In a further plot twist, the adult Eltham copper butterfly, for unknown reasons, largely lays its eggs on *dwarfed* sweet bursaria plants, not just any old sweet bursaria. (Just as Van Halen once requested that all brown M&Ms be removed from their backstage candy bowl, this snobby but fascinating butterfly has *needs,* somewhat confounding conservation efforts). The caterpillars strip the sweet bursaria plants of their leaves by night, feeding hungrily, and spend their days sheltering in the ant nest, where they remain protected from predators. They even see out the cold days of winter in these ant colonies, and ultimately pupate within the ant nest.

WHAT TO LOOK FOR A dark brown butterfly, about 25mm in wingspan with a panel of copper orange in each forewing and hindwing. The underwings are a silvery brown with faint leopard-spot-ish patterning. Caterpillars are a translucent pale green, and generally feed only at night, sheltering during the day.

LIFE CYCLE The adult female Eltham copper lays eggs on dwarf sweet bursaria plants. The eggs hatch, and the caterpillars feed nocturnally, sharing a kind of mutualistic relationship with local *Notoncus* ants. When ready, the larvae pupate in the nearby ant nest, developing there until the adults emerge in the warmer months.

WHERE TO LOOK There are just a few surviving populations of Eltham copper butterflies in Kiata, some small sites near Castlemaine, and the eponymous Melbourne/Naarm suburb of Eltham. This subspecies was thought to have gone extinct in the 1950s, however, it was re-discovered in the late 1980s, which motivated a campaign to preserve habitat and control weed spread. There are local conservation groups that will be able to provide localised information on seeing and supporting this species. Adult Eltham copper butterflies feed by day from flowers, especially those on or close to sweet bursaria plants. That said, the broader species, known as the dull copper, *P. pyrodiscus*, can be seen in far-east Victoria, eastern NSW and south-east Queensland, living in open woodlands, providing you with another opportunity to get to know this fascinating species.

WHEN TO LOOK Late spring through summer.

HABITAT HELP Protecting native bushland regions where sweet bursaria is abundant – especially in regions where the Eltham copper is still sighted – is essential to the survival of this species.

SIMILAR SPECIES The common grass-blue (*Zizinia otis*, pictured opposite) is a widespread example of another 'blues' butterfly, as is the southern purple azure (*Ogyris genoveva*, pictured opposite) seen in south-east Australia, or the fiery jewel (*Hypochrysops ignitus*, pictured opposite).

Pseudalmenus chlorinda

SILKY HAIRSTREAK

WAVY TAIL TIPS

IMPERIAL HAIRSTREAK

SILVERY UNDERSIDE TO WINGS

SILKY HAIRSTREAK CATERPILLAR

SILKY HAIRSTREAK BUTTERFLY

Picture yourself as an ant. In the harsh Australian bush, it's a tough life, even with three pairs of legs and the support of your colony. One day, climbing an acacia tree, you encounter a voluptuous and nice-smelling caterpillar that oozes a sugary syrup, which you can eat. Wouldn't you keep visiting that sugar daddy caterpillar? Especially since anything rich in energy is a hard-to-find resource, and the caterpillar is giving it away freely … or is it? These wily caterpillars know that having ants around provides some protection from predators. So, in exchange for a supply of sugar, the ants unwittingly give the caterpillar some security. Lycaenidae butterflies – known as the 'blues' – are pretty consistently associated with at least one, if not multiple 'attendant ant species'. These ant-caterpillar associations are often essential for Lycaenidae butterflies, and prove a reminder of the surreal paths evolution sometimes takes.

One of the more curious-looking members of the Lycaenidae family, the silky hairstreak is one of several 'hairstreak' butterflies, who all have strange, wavy extensions from their hindwing, like a crooked, smaller version of a swallowtail tip. The silky hairstreak is associated with only one species of ant (*Anonychomyrma biconvexa*). They also have a predilection for wattles as a food plant.

WHAT TO LOOK FOR A small (about 30mm wingspan) black, yellow and orange butterfly with wavy little extensions from the hindwing tips. The underside of the wings are a silvery white colour, with a dark band across both wings, and a red mark across the hindwing. The caterpillars are usually about 30mm long at maturity, and are white with black squiggly patterning.

LIFE CYCLE The silky hairstreak lays eggs on its preferred food plants (wattles), where there are often established colonies of their attendant ant species. After the eggs hatch, the caterpillars emerge and feed until ready to pupate. Much of their feeding time is accompanied by attendant ants who, in turn, feed from the sugary exudes that the caterpillars release. When ready, the larvae pupate in a nook or cranny (usually under the bark of the host acacia or a nearby tree) until the adults emerge.

WHERE TO LOOK Eastern Tasmania, Victoria and eastern NSW, with limited ranges in each of these states. They habituate mountainous areas and, as lovers of wattles, will prefer bushland reserves that have plenty of acacia species growing, such as silver, black and Ovens wattle.

WHEN TO LOOK Spring and summer (in Tasmania, you'll probably only see adult silky hairstreak butterflies in summer).

HABITAT HELP This butterfly relies on three things: certain wattle species as caterpillar food, *Anonychomyrma biconvexa* ants as 'guardians', and nearby old-growth gum trees which support these ant colonies. Protecting habitats from clearing, especially in areas where old-growth native trees remain, is a good way to support this species.

SIMILAR SPECIES Imperial hairstreak (*Jalmenus evagoras*, pictured opposite), found from Victoria, to eastern NSW and in south-east Queensland, yellow admiral (*see* p.17) and tailed emperor (*see* p.13).

Ocybadistes walkeri

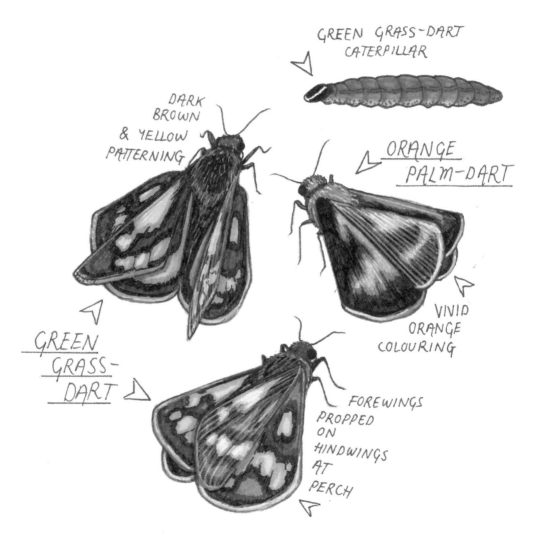

GREEN GRASS-DART
CATERPILLAR

DARK
BROWN
& YELLOW
PATTERNING

ORANGE
PALM-DART

VIVID
ORANGE
COLOURING

GREEN
GRASS-
DART

FOREWINGS
PROPPED
ON
HINDWINGS
AT
PERCH

GREEN GRASS-DART BUTTERFLY

The green grass-dart butterfly is a member of the family Hesperiidae, broadly known as the 'skippers'. Many of these butterflies look superficially similar, and it can often take an expert-level knowledge of wing patterns and sex-brands to correctly identify these species. However, most skipper butterflies have a distinctive body shape and behaviours, helping you to spot the family group quite easily. One likely skipper sighting is the widespread, ornate butterfly known as the green grass-dart. These tiny black and orange butterflies are found in open grasslands and parklands in northern and eastern Australia. Like many others in its family, they are slightly chunky-looking for a butterfly, compact, with angular wings, and antennae that are slightly hooked or pointed at their tip (many other butterflies have clubbed antennae). Skippers also have a distinctive pose, which you'll be able to see if you watch them land on dandelions or other flowering plants. When they come in to land, they prop their forewings on their hindwings, almost like the upturned tips of a jet plane's wings.

The name 'skipper' seems appropriate because when disturbed while feeding, these butterflies launch off their perch with immense speed, almost like they've sprung away rather than flown. This can make it a bit tricky to get a close look at them, but with patience you should succeed.

WHAT TO LOOK FOR Small (about 20mm wingspan) orange and dark brown butterflies, often flying over – or perched in – open areas of land. The caterpillars are green, with a darkened head, and a white line along each side of the body.

LIFE CYCLE Adults lay their eggs on native or introduced grasses, where they eventually hatch. The caterpillars emerge and feed at night, often hiding out in the curve of a grass blade during the day. When grown to about 20mm long, the caterpillars pupate amongst the grasses to later emerge as adults.

WHERE TO LOOK Tasmania, south-east SA, across Victoria, along the NSW and Queensland coasts, and in the northern NT. This species lives amongst both native and introduced grasses, so head to your local park or walking track, and look for green grass-darts anywhere with open grassy areas. I've had some luck seeing these butterflies along road verges where dandelions and other weedy flowers grow, which the adult butterflies often feed from.

WHEN TO LOOK Summer in the south of Australia, and year-round in the northern half of the country.

HABITAT HELP Protect existing and establish new areas of native grassland to support the many skipper butterfly species in Australia, including the green grass-dart.

SIMILAR SPECIES Many other skippers look very similar to the green grass-dart, with minute variations in wing patterns and colour, such as the orange palm-dart (*Cephrenes augiades*, pictured opposite), who has a similar range but is also found in WA. The common dart (*Ocybadistes flavovittatus*) has a similar range and appearance – like the orange palm-dart, these butterflies are tricky to distinguish from the green grass-dart.

Opodiphthera eucalypti

NOTE WHITE
TRIANGLE ON
FOREWING

EMPEROR
GUM MOTH

HELENA GUM
MOTH

YOUNG
EMPEROR
GUM MOTH
CATERPILLAR

LATE STAGE
EMPEROR
GUM MOTH
CATERPILLAR

EMPEROR GUM MOTH

Big wings? Check. Entrancing patterns? Check. Endearingly clumsy, extremely fluffy legs? Check. I know many people are inclined to be a bit fearful of moths, but a lovely gateway species into moth appreciation is the emperor gum moth. These beautiful creatures have curved wings patterned with large eye spots (likely intended to intimidate predators). You may have been lucky enough to encounter one flapping against the window of your kitchen or verandah light if you live along the east coast of Australia. Adult emperor gum moths do not feed, instead relying on reserves of energy they consumed as caterpillars (read: snacking on lots of eucalypt leaves). After emerging, these moths seek a mate, living for only a few days. Often their delicate wings will grow tattered over their short adulthood, so if you see an emperor gum moth with untarnished wings, it's likely that it has recently hatched from its pupa. My sister and I collected these caterpillars when we were kids, and watching them grow was mesmerising.

This moth is part of the Saturniidae family, a group that contains some of the largest and most dazzlingly patterned moths in the world (such as the Hercules moth, see p.ix). The name Saturniidae always feels appropriate to me when looking at these huge, lustrous creatures whose spectacular patterns remind me of the rings of Saturn, or the swirling storms and Big Red Spot of Jupiter.

WHAT TO LOOK FOR A big (with a wingspan of about 100mm) rusty-brown moth with eye-spots on its wings (some can even appear a little bit yellow, depending on the season and location). Males generally have larger, feathery antennae, which are likely used to sense the pheromones of nearby female moths. The caterpillars go through a few colour stages as they feed and mature into vibrant green-blue grubs.

LIFE CYCLE The emperor gum moth lays its eggs in the canopy of a gum tree, providing the ultimate meal to a newly hatched caterpillar: eucalypt leaves. The caterpillars feed and grow until they are ready to pupate, at which point they build a leathery silken cocoon, where they remain until ready to emerge as an adult.

WHERE TO LOOK Eastern Queensland, eastern NSW, across Victoria, and in south-east SA. These moths are also sometimes spotted in the NT. Head to local bush reserves or parks where eucalyptus trees grow. Emperor gum moth adults are nocturnal, so if you head out with friends or family for a night-walk with some headtorches, you be able to spot an adult flying about. Look in spring and summer during the day amongst eucalypt leaves where you might find caterpillars.

WHEN TO LOOK Most common in spring, summer and early autumn.

SIMILAR SPECIES Helena Gum moth (*Opodiphthera helena*, pictured opposite), with a similar range to the emperor gum moth, is also found across Tasmania and in south-western WA. The southern moon moth (*see* p.46) also looks a little similar to the emperor gum moth.

Phyllodes imperialis (subspecies *smithersi*)

LEAF-LIKE
FOREWING

PINK
PATCH ON
HINDWING

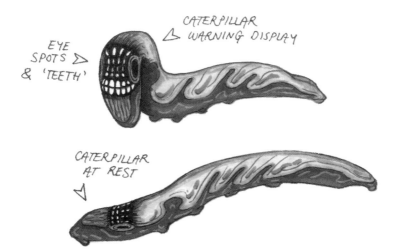

CATERPILLAR
WARNING DISPLAY

EYE
SPOTS
& 'TEETH'

CATERPILLAR
AT REST

SOUTHERN PINK UNDERWING MOTH

Imagine wandering in your garden on a clear night and, when inspecting a dried leaf on a vine, you are surprised to discover it is, in fact, a moth. When it lifts off from the vine, you see only its forewings resemble dead leaves – each hindwing has a patch of bright fuchsia, visible as it flaps away. This is the endangered and spectacular southern pink underwing moth. Several other species of moths in the Erebidae family are known as fruit-sucking moths (they, vampire-style, poke their proboscis through the skin of your beloved oranges to suck out the juices. Cue organ solo). However, the southern pink underwing moth is more like a Halloween party attendee wearing gummy teeth, instead of true fangs. These moths only feed on damaged or rotten fruit, as they don't have strong enough mouthparts to pierce the hard skins of healthy fruit. Their forewings camouflage them well against native foliage and, if disturbed, they can spread their upper wings to reveal the bright pink patch on their hindwings, hopefully shocking their pursuer, and buying them a little more time to fly off.

As if these night-feeding critters weren't already striking enough, the larvae of the southern pink underwing moth have some groovy strategies for defence. The caterpillar, if disturbed, rears up its mid-section, revealing a pattern over its back that looks like a pair of eyes and a row of teeth.

WHAT TO LOOK FOR A moth with a wingspan of about 100mm, with a brown, leaf-like forewing, coming to a curved-back tip. When the forewing moves, the vivid pink hindwing is displayed. The mature caterpillars are a rusty red-brown colour and, when startled, show patterns that resemble eyespots and teeth.

LIFE CYCLE These moths exclusively lay eggs on the carronia vine, making them vulnerable to habitat loss, especially in the rapidly diminishing pockets of subtropical rainforest they call home. The eggs hatch and the caterpillars feed, grow, pupate, then emerge as adults. I hope these harmless little fruit-vampires garner more attention and support.

WHERE TO LOOK There are small remnant populations in south-east Queensland and north-east NSW, including on Bundjalung Country (Northern Rivers region, NSW) and on Gumbaynggirr Country (near Coffs Harbour, NSW). This subspecies is endangered and rare to find, though the broader species, the imperial fruit-sucking moth (*Phyllodes imperialis*), can be seen along the Queensland coast.

WHEN TO LOOK Late spring and summer.

HABITAT HELP Residents within the local range of the southern pink underwing moth are encouraged to plant carronia vine (*Carronia multisepalea*), especially if there is remnant native rainforest nearby. This will provide essential food and habitat to the moths.

SIMILAR SPECIES The green fruit-piercing moth (*Eudocima salaminia*), can be seen along the NSW and Queensland coasts.

Zelotypia stacyi

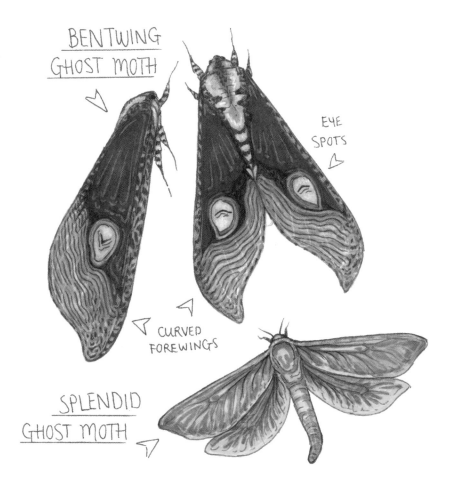

BENTWING
GHOST MOTH

EYE
SPOTS

CURVED
FOREWINGS

SPLENDID
GHOST MOTH

BENTWING GHOST MOTH

Meet the gloriously surreal bentwing ghost moth. Though these elusive creatures appear infrequently as adults, many specimens are found in entomology collections around the world due to their enormous size and elegance. The larvae of these moths feed on native hardwood trees, such as red iron gum, rose gum and Sydney blue gum, remaining unseen within the trunk while they develop. Some of these woods were used to reinforce shafts in early Australian coal mines. These wooden reinforcements would sometimes harbour several larvae of the bentwing swift moths which, indifferent to their location underground, would merrily pupate. With time (sometimes a matter of years), the pupae would hatch, and *huge* bentwing ghost moths would emerge from the wood, where they would fly around in the ghastly underground mine shafts. This image is so cinematic that I can't help but love these moths for their creepy, ghostly history. The resourceful coal miners, recognising how distinctive these creatures are, gathered specimens and sold them to Sydney-based wildlife collectors to make some lucre on the side.

The adult moths have no mouthparts, so they do not feed – instead, they live only a short period of time, seeking out a mate, laying eggs, then dying off, hence their rare sightings as adults.

WHAT TO LOOK FOR The bentwing ghost moth can have a wingspan over 200mm. They have brown, patterned forewings (including eyespots), and hindwings that are a faint pinkish-orange colour. When folded at perch, the forewings disguise these moths well, making them look much like dead leaves. Larvae feed and remain within trees as they develop.

LIFE CYCLE Species in the ghost moth family Hepialidae are known for their enthusiastic egg production, often laying an *immense* amount of eggs after mating (commonly in the thousands). One author, Tim R. New, after watching a species of ghost moth laying eggs, said he 'henceforth thought of them as the 'B-52s' of the insect world'. This cracked me up. Though little has been observed of the life cycle of the bentwing ghost moth, it is likely that after hatching, the larvae burrow into eucalypt trees where they feed and grow until ready to pupate. After pupating in the wood, the developed moths emerge for a brief adulthood.

WHERE TO LOOK These moths are occasionally spotted in the damp eucalypt-dominated forests in eastern NSW, around Sydney/Warrang and Newcastle.

WHEN TO LOOK The adult moths emerge and are active in late summer and autumn, though their emergence is fleeting and varied, depending on conditions.

SIMILAR SPECIES The bentwing ghost moth is the only member of its genus, *Zelotypia*, in Australia, and thus is quite distinctive. Its relative, the common splendid ghost moth (*Aenetus eximia*, pictured opposite), can be seen from southern Queensland to Tasmania, but is much smaller and green in colour. You might also confuse some species of ghost moths with members of the hawkmoth family (*see* p.43), which have a similar body shape.

Metura elongatus

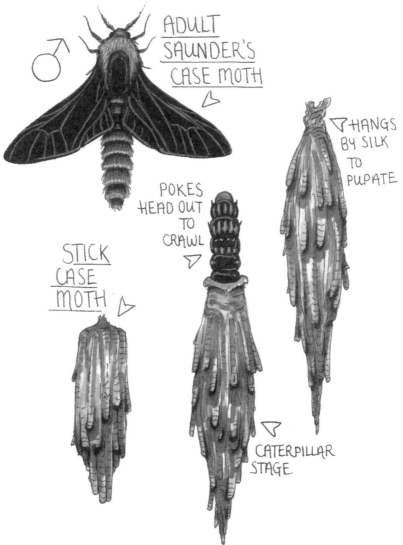

♂ ADULT SAUNDER'S CASE MOTH

HANGS BY SILK TO PUPATE

POKES HEAD OUT TO CRAWL

STICK CASE MOTH

CATERPILLAR STAGE

SAUNDER'S CASE MOTH

You may have wandered out to the garden to find a new, strange-looking bundle of sticks hanging from the branch of a tree, or from the wall of your house. Or maybe you, like I did, wandered out to the hills hoist to find a weird little bundle of twigs hanging from one of the towels. Grab your detective cap, Dr Watson, it's time to solve the mystery of the Case of the Case Moth. This bundle of twigs isn't just some strange bit of debris, but is the home to a moth, known as a case moth, or bagworm.

Caterpillars in this family, Psychidae, cleverly build cases – both defensive and camouflaging – usually made from twigs, bark, leaves and their own silk. They use the tiny protruding fore-section of their bodies (head and thorax) to crawl about and feed, a bit like a snail. These caterpillars are impressively mobile for someone dragging the equivalent of a caravan behind them. If heat or movement is sensed nearby, the caterpillars retreat back into their case until the danger has passed. Most species have a predilection for certain building materials, and the Saunder's case moth forms a home from overlain twigs and silk. Elementary, my dear Watson.

WHAT TO LOOK FOR The male adult moths have a wingspan of about 30mm, and are quite fluffy, with an orange-and-black-striped abdomen. The caterpillars (and house-bound adult females) can be recognised by their twig-laden cases. The cylindrical case is usually about 50-70mm long, made up of overlain layers of twigs in a silky 'glue'.

LIFE CYCLE Strangely enough, only the male moths emerge from the case. The females never develop any wings, remaining inside their little home until they lay eggs and die, undergoing the whole process without leaving their twig-prison. After hatching, the tiny caterpillars descend from the case using their silk. The breeze usually blows them several metres away where they commence building their own case. Having eaten and grown a sufficient amount, the caterpillar will find a more permanent site of attachment for the case, and will pupate inside. Males emerge to seek a female, while females rely on pheromones to draw in mobile males. Adults do not feed, usually living only a matter of days.

WHERE TO LOOK Saunder's case moths are common in both urban and bushland habitats along Australia's east coast. Wander around your garden or local park and look for little bundles of twigs hanging in trees, or sometimes from power poles or brick walls. The larvae are quite fond of various introduced species in urbanised areas (including cypress).

WHEN TO LOOK Year-round, however temperature conditions, avoiding predation or illness (they can be attacked by fungi inside their cases, or parasitised by wasps, like ichneumon wasps, *see* p.63), and food availability all impact the development of Saunder's case moths, so populations will fluctuate.

SIMILAR SPECIES Most case moths have similar habits to the Saunder's case moth. The stick case moth (*Clania lewinii*, pictured opposite) is found in NSW, Victoria and Tasmania, and usually makes their case longer, and with more parallel sticks than the Saunder's case moth.

Chelepteryx collesi

LARGE
CURVED
WINGS

BATWING MOTH CATERPILLAR

BATWING MOTH

If you're lucky in late summer or the autumn months, you may have found one of these enormous moths drawn to the lights around your house. Batwing moths are short-lived – they don't have the mouthparts for feeding, instead they rely on energy reserves they stored as a hungry caterpillar to sustain their mission for reproduction. Pretty much all moths in this family, Anthelidae (aka 'hairy bear' moths), never feed as adults, but instead emerge from their cocoons to quickly find a mate, then die off. Though the adults seem delicate and fleeting, the survivalist cunning of this moth is manifest in those hungry caterpillars. The name 'hairy bear', despite its superficial cuteness, actually refers to the extremely painful and irritating hairs that the caterpillars are covered with. These spikes can break off and lodge in any creature who hassles them while they're trying to feed. Even in the cocoon phase, batwing moths keep their defences at the ready. The cocoons look a little like seed pods, made of tough silk-like material. You can sometimes spot them on tree trunks where the caterpillar has spent the warm months of the year feeding. To ensure their beauty sleep isn't disturbed, the caterpillar pushes its stinging hairs through the silk, creating an external palisade of nasty spikes outside its cocoon.

When you type in the Latin name for this species on a scholarly engine, the top result is usually a medical journal describing victims who have encountered the painful hairs of a batwing moth caterpillar. This effect – the injury by contact with butterflies, moths or their larvae – is called Lepidopterism and the batwing moth is famous for it. No one's bugging this little caterpillar while it's doing its thing. No. One.

WHAT TO LOOK FOR A large rusty red, grey and black patterned moth, about 120mm in wingspan. Males have large, feathery antennae, while females are bigger and have more slender antennae. The caterpillars, when nearly mature, are about 10-12mm long. These grubs have black and white stripes and, most importantly, are adorned with nasty red spikes.

LIFE CYCLE Eggs are usually lain amongst eucalypt trees. Caterpillars hatch and feed over summer, then pupate close to their feeding location. They remain in their cocoon until the adults emerge, who survive just long enough to mate and lay eggs.

WHERE TO LOOK Along the east and south coasts of south-east Australia, from Victoria up to southern Queensland. Try parklands, bushland reserves or farm windbreaks where eucalypt trees grow.

WHEN TO LOOK Caterpillars are usually active in summer, while adult moths appear in late summer and autumn.

SIMILAR SPECIES The variable anthelid (*Anthela varia*) is another large moth of the same family found along the east coast. Processionary caterpillars (*see* p.37) are also covered in stinging hairs.

Ochrogaster lunifer

ALYAWARR LANGUAGE
ingeth (pronounced ing-IT-a) ('processionary caterpillar').

WARLPIRI LANGUAGE
pakurujunkurrpa (BAH-koo-roo-JUNE-koor-pah) ('processionary caterpillar').

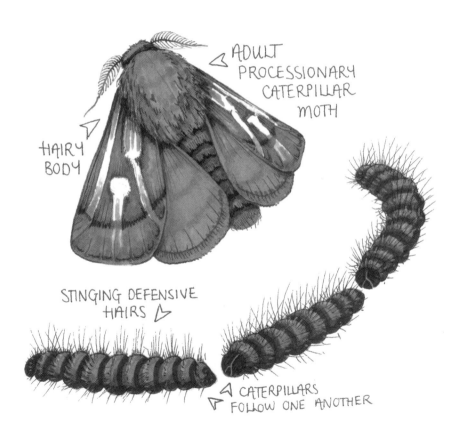

ADULT PROCESSIONARY CATERPILLAR MOTH

HAIRY BODY

STINGING DEFENSIVE HAIRS

CATERPILLARS FOLLOW ONE ANOTHER

PROCESSIONARY CATERPILLAR

Imagine one day you're walking through the bush, and you notice an undulating conga line of hairy caterpillars crossing the trail, each grub following the next so closely that they are touching tip-to-tail. What would you make of it? Well, you have encountered the strange and marvellous (and slightly scary) processionary caterpillar. The relatively nondescript adult moths have only a brief lifespan. However, the caterpillars use some interesting tactics for survival.

The caterpillars are definitely extroverts, hanging out in peer groups for most of their development, either feeding in the canopy, or loitering in the nests they spin together. Their nests are made of silk and debris (and a fair share of insect poop, known as frass). This structure serves as a temporary shelter for the caterpillars between feeding sessions, earning this species the alternate name: 'bag-shelter moth'. When it comes time to change trees to continue feeding, the caterpillars form an orderly line, following one after the other, forming a metres-long queue to head for the next tasty wattle tree. Sometimes processionary caterpillars accidentally form a circle formation, where they follow one another in an endless Sisyphean mission – bless their furry little bodies. However, those hairs aren't just for show. Like the batwing moth (*see* p.35), their hairs (even on the adult moths) are highly irritating and can cause nasty dermatitis if touched.

WHAT TO LOOK FOR Hairy grey-brown caterpillars with a rusty-coloured head, usually about 40mm long. The adult moths are brown-grey, with a wingspan of about 50mm, with two white stripes and a white dot on each forewing.

LIFE CYCLE The adult female moths lay a clutch of eggs at the base of a food plant, most often a wattle tree. After laying, they cover their eggs with their pain-inducing, irritating body hairs – a defensive barrier to protect their eggs. Once hatched, the caterpillars climb into the canopy to feed at night, and retreat to their silken bag-nest to rest between feedings. The caterpillars, when fully grown, burrow into the soil, where they create a cocoon, and pupate over winter. The adults, emerging in spring and summer, live only a few days, as they do not feed. Instead, they focus on reproducing as soon as they can.

WHERE TO LOOK The processionary caterpillar can be seen all over Australia, excluding Tasmania, though they tend to be more common in coastal forests. I have mostly spotted them when bushwalking by first noticing their silken 'nests' in acacias. Head to your local bushland reserve or national park, or walk along watercourses where there is remnant native bush.

WHEN TO LOOK Adults emerge in spring and early summer.

SIMILAR SPECIES Many other moth species have hairy caterpillars, including the batwing moth, and it's possible that some other species also have processional habits when moving between feeding sites. When I walk in the High Country, I often see several varieties of hairy caterpillars rushing along the path.

Alcides metaurus

COLOURS OF
ADULTS VARY

BANDS
OF COLOUR

ORNATE
HINDWINGS

ZODIAC MOTH
CATERPILLAR

ZODIAC MOTH

Looking at a zodiac moth is a bit like looking into the psychedelic opening credits of *Doctor Who* (one of the 1960s or '70s episodes, to be exact). They are largely black, but are patterned with dizzying pinkish-yellow concentric circles that cross over both wings. The zodiac moth tends to feed and rest amongst tropical rainforests in Queensland, for all intensive purposes behaving like a butterfly. They perch with wings out flat like a butterfly, rather than streamlined back like lots of other moths. They even have slender antennae, and short extensions at the tip of each hindwing which make them look a bit like a swallowtail butterfly (*see* p.1). However, they are actually one of several peculiar 'in between' species that look very much like a butterfly, but are in fact classified as a day-flying moth.

The origin of the name 'zodiac' possibly refers to the repeated arcs of patterning across the moth's wings, which are reminiscent of the belt of zodiac constellations that encircle the sky. Zodiac moths feed during the day from flowering plants, often hanging out close to the host plants – usually rainforest vines – where they lay their eggs. As a species found only in tropical far-north Queensland, these moths aren't widespread but are sometimes seen in large numbers, aggregating to overwinter much like the common crow butterfly (*see* p.11).

WHAT TO LOOK FOR A large black and yellow-pink moth with a wingspan of nearly 100mm. (There is a fair bit of colour variation in the adults – some may have a blue-ish hue to their wings instead of pink-yellow, or even a much paler cream colouring.) The underside of the wings show more concentric circles in pale green and black, and the abdomen has a bright red-orange strip along its underside. The caterpillars go through several colour stages, but at maturity are striped with black and red.

LIFE CYCLE Adult moths lay eggs close to food plants (often *Omphalea* spp. and *Endospermum* spp., both plants that are found in rainforest), on which the caterpillars feed when they hatch. After feeding and growing, the caterpillars pupate until the adult moths emerge to seek a mate.

WHERE TO LOOK Along the far-north Queensland coast from Cape York to Darumbal Country (around Rockhampton), with seasonal variations in numbers. There are also some recorded sightings in the NT, but there is little information on how consistent their presence is there. The adults feed on flower nectar, and usually remain close to *Omphalea* and *Endospermum* species of plants, so keep an eye out in areas of flowering rainforest where these plants grow.

WHEN TO LOOK Year-round, sometimes gathering in large numbers over winter in Queensland.

HABITAT HELP Growing and protecting endemic *Omphalea* and *Endospermum* plants are a good way to support zodiac moths.

SIMILAR SPECIES Another tropical patterned moth, *Lyssa macleayi*, is in the same family, Uraniidae, and is also found on the coast of northern Queensland.

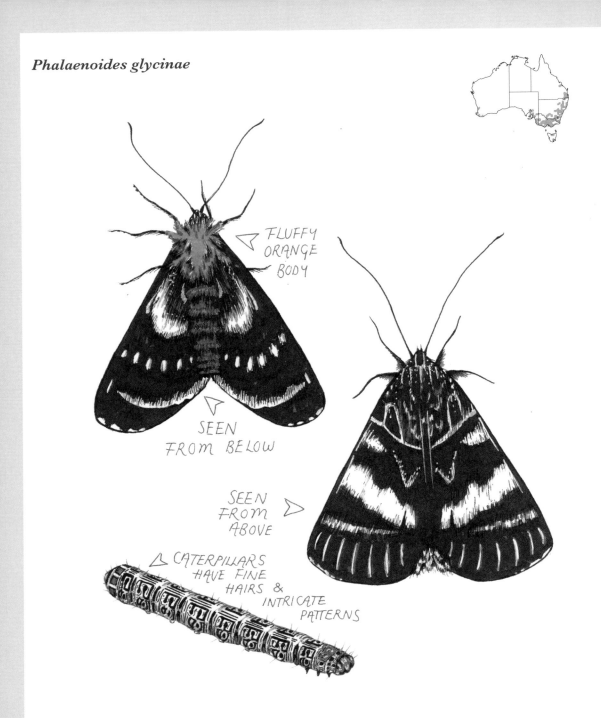

Phalaenoides glycinae

FLUFFY ORANGE BODY

SEEN FROM BELOW

SEEN FROM ABOVE

CATERPILLARS HAVE FINE HAIRS & INTRICATE PATTERNS

AUSTRALIAN GRAPEVINE MOTH

If you live in a temperate climate, you might have sat on your verandah with a cuppa in hand and noticed black, hairy caterpillars feeding off the new-formed foliage of your grapevine. The caterpillars are the larval stage of the Australian grapevine moth, who decimate grapevine leaves with voracious hunger. The adult moths can be seen in spring and summer, often hurriedly laying eggs on grapevines and neighbouring plants with reckless abandon. Last spring, one fastidious female moth visited the grapevine on my verandah for several days in a row, and I was able to watch her land and bend her abdomen into a 'c' shape, allowing her to stick tiny eggs onto the grapevine. She appeared frantic, but I think many moths have that energy, especially when it comes to egg-laying time.

Although these moths are native to Australia and are able to feed on native grapevines, they have developed a proclivity for imported varieties, sometimes causing massive damage to commercial crops. In a feat of human misdirection, the common myna bird was introduced to Australia in the 1860s to try to control the populations of these moth larvae, along with a bunch of other pest insect species. However, the common myna has done little to impact populations of the grapevine moth. Instead, since introduction, common mynas have gained pest status, while the Australian grapevine moth continues to thrive. For a similar tale, *see* p.87 about the greyback cane beetle and the cane toad strategy.

WHAT TO LOOK FOR A black and white moth with an orange-and-black-striped abdomen (of wingspan about 40mm). The grapevine caterpillars are patterned with white, black and red, and grow to about 40mm in length.

LIFE CYCLE Adult moths generally emerge in spring to mate, then lay eggs on food plants (read: your tasty grapevine). The eggs hatch in late spring and caterpillars feed until ready to pupate. When seasons are favourable, sometimes there may be several generations of adult moths produced over spring and summer. For those that pupate as the weather starts to cool, they can enter a state called 'diapause', where they literally pause their development, waiting until the weather warms, days lengthen and – most importantly – tender new leaves grow on your grapevine. The adults only live for a couple of weeks, subsisting off nectar.

WHERE TO LOOK South-west WA, south-east SA, across Victoria, Tasmania, in eastern NSW and along the coast of southern Queensland. If you have a grapevine in your garden, or know a local garden that has vines, head there in spring to try to spot some fluttering movement amongst the leaves. Grapevine moths have also been observed eating native plants, including native grapevine (*Cissus hypoglauca*) and love creepers (*Glycine clandestina*).

WHEN TO LOOK Spring and summer.

SIMILAR SPECIES Many species of tiger moths (subfamily Arctiinae, *see* p.49) have similar black, white and orange patterns to the grapevine moth.

Hippotion celerio

ALYWARR LANGUAGE
antyarlk (pronounced un-JARLK-a), (type of caterpillar, elephant grub, whitelined hawk moth, yeperenye caterpillar, Australian striped hawkmoth, *Hyles livornicoides*).

WARLPIRI LANGUAGE
jinji-marlu-marlu (JIN-jee-MAH-loo-MAH-loo); *pinta pinta* (PIN-ter-PIN-ter); *yirntilyapilyapi* (YEERN-til-yah-PILL-yah-pee), (all terms used for 'butterfly', 'moth', or 'airplane').

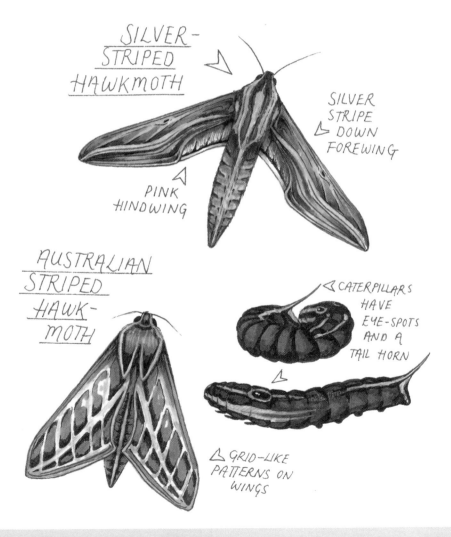

SILVER-STRIPED HAWKMOTH

SILVER STRIPE DOWN FOREWING

PINK HINDWING

AUSTRALIAN STRIPED HAWK-MOTH

CATERPILLARS HAVE EYE-SPOTS AND A TAIL HORN

GRID-LIKE PATTERNS ON WINGS

SILVER-STRIPED HAWKMOTH

The silver-striped hawkmoth, found across Australia, is also a global citizen, appearing in many parts of Africa, Europe and Asia. They are specialised creatures, migrating from northern climes to more southern areas during warmer months. They are marvellous fliers, allowing them to hover over blossoms, where their wings move so quickly they become a blur of motion. To feed, rather than landing, they hover in place over the flower, and unfurl their impressively long proboscis, which can be double the length of their body. Thus, they can use their straw-like tongue to drink nectar without ever setting a miniature foot on a petal. These moths are called 'hawkmoths' or 'sphinx moths', are in the family Sphingidae. There are about 60 species of hawkmoths known in Australia, many of them very beautiful or strange in appearance, like the gardenia bee hawkmoth (*see* p.45). There are also numerous hawkmoths found overseas, including the fabled death's head hawkmoth of Thomas Harris' *Silence of the Lambs* (1988) – a little something for your next trivia night.

To assist with their skilful flight, hawkmoths make use of a specialised organ known as the Johnston's organ. This is located in the antennae of all Australian insects, where it serves a number of different functions, including assessing the wingbeats of a potential mate in fruit flies, and allowing honey bees to communicate through dance. In the case of the hawkmoths, it assists with stabilising their flight, ensuring they can seek out, hover over, dart away from and return again to flowers with amazing accuracy. Some hawkmoths are prized for their unique ability to effectively pollinate certain orchids, or for their role in pollinating commercial crops that have long tubular flowers, such as papaya.

WHAT TO LOOK FOR A brown-grey-and-cream coloured moth, though sometimes the adult moth looks faintly greenish. Each forewing has a cream edge, and the hindwing has a faint blush-coloured patch close to the abdomen. The mature caterpillars are dark grey, with a pale stripe down either side of the body, eye spots towards the head, and a dark 'horn' at the tip of the tail (characteristic of many hawkmoth caterpillars).

LIFE CYCLE An adult silver-striped hawkmoth usually lays eggs on a variety of food plants, though they tend to have a proclivity for grapevines (these moths are also known as 'vine hawkmoths'). The eggs hatch, and the caterpillars feed on plant matter, growing in size, until they crawl down to the ground level to pupate either in the soil or amongst the leaf litter, emerging later as adults.

WHERE TO LOOK Across Australia, but they are especially successful in northern regions, while they are only occasionally seen in southern regions, including Tasmania. Head to gardens, parks, bush reserves or suburban gardens where the moths tend to become active at dusk.

WHEN TO LOOK Spring and summer in the south, year-round in the north.

SIMILAR SPECIES Convolvus hawk moth (*Agrius convolvuli*) has a similar distribution, and the Australian striped hawkmoth (*Hyles livornicoides*, pictured opposite) is found across Australia.

Cephonodes kingii

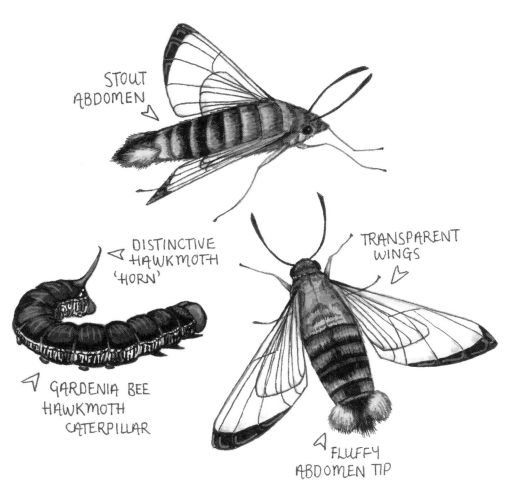

STOUT
ABDOMEN

DISTINCTIVE
HAWKMOTH
'HORN'

TRANSPARENT
WINGS

GARDENIA BEE
HAWKMOTH
CATERPILLAR

FLUFFY
ABDOMEN TIP

GARDENIA BEE HAWKMOTH

I hope you can imagine the following words in the ever-charming voice of Sir David Attenborough: meet the delightful gardenia bee hawkmoth. Is it a bee? Is it a hawk? Is it a moth? Or, perhaps, is it a glorious amalgamation of all of them? This hairy, green, bumblebee-like creature is, in fact, a day-flying moth. It is part of the family Sphingidae, the group known as the 'hawkmoths', all of whom are renowned for their speedy flight. Hawkmoths are excellent at hovering, especially above flowers, into which they extend their long proboscis to feed.

The gardenia bee hawkmoth is no exception, only it is made even more memorable by its bumblebee-ish appearance, with a striped yellow abdomen and transparent wings. Like the golden native drone fly (*see* p.155), looking like a bee is probably advantageous, because predators might think you have a nasty sting with which you can defend yourself. These moths readily cruise flower to flower in broad daylight, hovering over each to feed, hopefully avoiding the hassles of birds and other predators. The gardenia bee hawkmoth is yet another example of the many beautiful Australian moths that are diurnal (day-flying).

WHAT TO LOOK FOR A large green and yellow bee-like moth, with a wingspan of about 40mm. The body of the gardenia bee hawkmoth is a bit bigger and rounder than the abdomens of most other moths, and has bands of black and yellow across its tip. The caterpillars are almost as spectacular as the adults, with black and white patterning, red dots down the sides of the body, and a long horn on the tail (a marker of the hawkmoth family). The caterpillars grow to about 60mm long.

LIFE CYCLE Adults lay eggs on or near favoured plant species – often gardenia and other members of Rubiaceae – where the eggs hatch and the caterpillars readily feed. After feeding and growing, the caterpillar heads into the soil to pupate. Once metamorphosis is complete, adult bee hawkmoths emerge to buzz merrily away.

WHERE TO LOOK These moths can be seen along the coast of Queensland and NSW, with some limited sightings further south. Look in lush suburban or botanic gardens, or bushland with plenty of flowering plants where adults might be looking for nectar. The caterpillars feed on a variety of native and introduced plants.

WHEN TO LOOK Spring and summer.

SIMILAR SPECIES Other hawkmoths have similar habits around flowers, though most of them are nocturnal, unlike the sunshine-loving gardenia bee hawkmoth.

Agrotis infusa

YUGAMBEH LANGUAGE
banjalahm (pronounced BUN-jah-LAHM)
('moth').

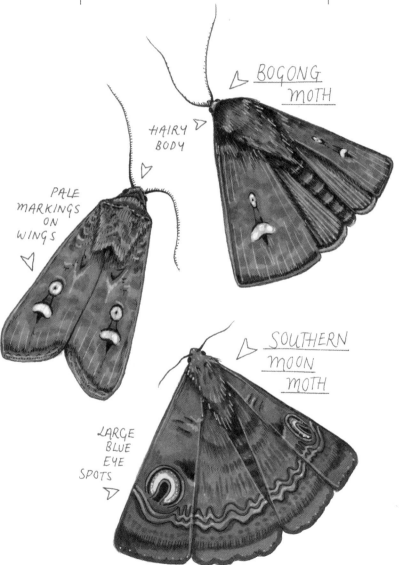

BOGONG MOTH

HAIRY BODY

PALE MARKINGS ON WINGS

SOUTHERN MOON MOTH

LARGE BLUE EYE SPOTS

BOGONG MOTH

While these unassuming insects may appear to be just another brown moth drawn to your porch light, their collective cultural and economic impact is enormous. They are known for their large springtime migrations in the Australian Alps, where they are able to escape the heat of summer. When winter rolls around, they migrate out to the lower-altitude plains of Queensland, in northern NSW and even in South Australia. They lay their eggs amongst crops, where the hatched larvae – known as 'black cutworms' – feed, vexing farmers. As the temperature turns warmer in spring, these larvae pupate and the newly emerged adult moths obey their instinctual urges and retreat up into the higher altitudes of the mountains. There, bogong moths spend their summer secluded in cooler caves and crannies of the alpine areas. (This over-summering is called 'aestivation'.)

Annual summer gatherings in the High Country of south-east Australia saw First Peoples gather to prepare feasts using bogong moths (*see* p.vi). Unfortunately, these mass bogong moth migrations have significantly decreased in recent years, likely due to drought, light pollution and pesticide use in agricultural pastures, where the larval stages of these insects feed.

WHAT TO LOOK FOR Bogong moths are silvery-brown, with a wingspan of about 40mm. Their wings have a longitudinal dark streak, marked with two paler dots. The larvae are an oily-grey coloured caterpillar, with a pale underbelly and legs.

LIFE CYCLE Adult female moths lay eggs near food plants, such as capeweed or a variety of commercial crops. Upon hatching, the larvae, true to their name 'black cutworms', emerge from the soil at night, 'cut' plants off near their base by chewing them, then retreat back to the ground to finish munching the foliage they've claimed. When grown, the larvae pupate in the soil, until the adult bogong moths emerge. Adult moths feed on flower nectar to sustain themselves.

WHERE TO LOOK Bogong moths can be seen in many areas of Australia, but are much more densely concentrated in south-east SA, Victoria, Tasmania, NSW and south-east Queensland. If you are in the High Country over spring or early summer, you might see moths in flight at twilight (take a torch). When I have been lucky enough to see bogong moths in the mountains, they have mostly been above the treeline. They are also sometimes suburban visitors, so check out any nondescript brown moths around your house and surrounds.

WHEN TO LOOK Spring to early summer, depending on seasonal variation. Not all bogong moths migrate – those in the more climactically wet areas of southern Queensland and in some areas of WA seem to stay put.

HABITAT HELP More information is needed to understand the seasonal movements of bogong moths and their impact on mountain-dwelling animals, such as the critically endangered mountain pygmy possum. You can use SWIFFT's online moth tracker to note any sightings of bogong moths (*see* p.203).

SIMILAR SPECIES Southern moon moth (*Dosypodia selenophora*, pictured opposite), seen across Australia, is often mistaken for the bogong moth as a regular house visitor.

Creatonotos gangis

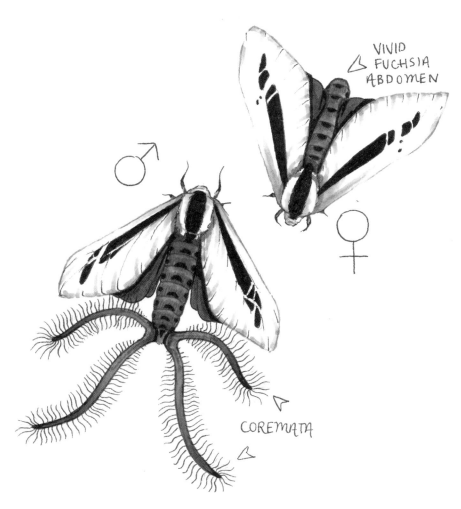

VIVID
FUCHSIA
ABDOMEN

COREMATA

BAPHOMET MOTH

'Baphomet', for which this moth is named, refers to an occult deity who has done the historic rounds. First, seemingly worshipped by the Knight's Templar, then the Freemasons, Baphomet was later adopted for worship by the infamous British occultist Alistair Crowley. Baphomet was said to be a hermaphroditic, goat-headed creature with large horns. The name has been applied to this moth because, I suppose, those abdominal 'tentacles' were mistaken for devilish horns. Only male Baphomet moths have these organs, known as 'coremata', which despite their supernatural appearance, are actually just a romantic prop used to disperse chemicals that draw in nearby lady-moths.

Males, when seeking a mate, will usually find a vertical perch on which to hang. Here, abdomen pointing down, the little moth spreads its wings to expose its abdomen. Then it uses both air and internal muscles to unfurl the coremata from its abdomen, where they can disperse pheromones into the air. Ideally, a nearby female will pick up on these pheromones and find him appealing. In actuality, several species of moths and butterflies have similar coremata (sometimes called hair-pencils), but the Baphomet moths have particularly large and striking appendages. To ensure their future efforts at wooing, young male caterpillars must hungrily munch up as many alkaloid-rich plants as they can. These alkaloids are found in certain plant groups (e.g. *Senecio* spp., daisies, and borage plants), and they impact both the size of the moth's coremata, and the quality of pheromones they produce. So, as a Baphomet moth, your chances for romance are causally related to eating your vegetables before your dessert.

WHAT TO LOOK FOR A sleek black-and-white moth, with a wingspan of about 40mm. When the white-and-black patterned wings are parted, the bright pink-red abdomen, lined with black dots, is exposed. Males only unfurl their coremata when seeking a mate, so you might not always be lucky enough to see their surreal abdominal tentacles on display. The caterpillars are hairy with a pale stripe running down their back.

LIFE CYCLE After mating, a female Baphomet moth will lay a row of eggs on a variety of food plants. The caterpillars hatch, feed, grow, form a cocoon in which to pupate, then emerge as an adult.

WHERE TO LOOK Baphomet moths can be seen sparsely across the northern coast of Australia, around to south-east Queensland. Look for them in or adjacent to bushland areas. They've been known to land on fly screens and windows at night, perhaps drawn there by artificial lights.

WHEN TO LOOK Year-round.

SIMILAR SPECIES The Baphomet moth is part of the tiger moth subfamily (Arctiinae), whose members mostly have white or yellow-and-black markings. Donovan's tiger moth (*Aloa marginata*) is a similar-looking moth (about 30mm long) that also displays coremata, and is seen around the coast of mainland Australia.

Synemon plana

DARK
FOREWINGS ▷

♀

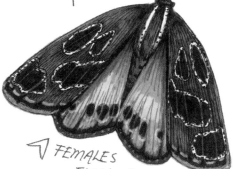

◁ FEMALES
FLASH BRIGHT
HINDWINGS

♂

MALES
◁ HAVE DULLER
HINDWINGS

GOLDEN SUN MOTH

These day-flying moths are a striking species, but live only a matter of days – the majority of their lives are spent as larvae, feeding underground on native grasses. Despite the brevity of their adult lives, golden sun moths have provided a symbol for the protection – and hopefully regeneration – of native grasslands, even as small remnants in urban areas.

The golden sun moth has provoked a fair bit of attention in recent years, as it occupies native grasslands, which, despite being very fragmented, partially extend into suburban regions of cities in Australia's south-east. The majority of these grasslands – 95 per cent, it is estimated – have been highly modified, if not outright destroyed, by weed encroachment, agricultural development and urban advance. Reserves in both Melbourne and Canberra have been created with the partial motivation of protecting existing habitat or populations of the golden sun moth, and in multiple cases in the ACT, caterpillars and pupa were translocated by hand ahead of a building development. Translocation, in this case, is literally carrying caterpillars and pupae to a new site where they will hopefully survive. There is limited evidence on whether translocation efforts actually work to preserve populations, but they are a first step towards better recognition of grasslands as sites that support ecologically significant species.

WHAT TO LOOK FOR A moth with dark brown-grey forewings and clubbed antennae, about 30mm in wingspan. Females have bright yellow hindwings. Caterpillars spend most of their development and even pupate underground, therefore they are hard to spot.

LIFE CYCLE Adult female moths rely on their bright hindwings to attract males. After mating, the poor-flying female moths lay eggs around the base of grasses. The feeble flight of the females has probably intensified how fragmented the populations have become, as they basically only lay eggs within moth-walking distance of their mating site. (Little fluffy moth legs can only take you so far). The caterpillars burrow into the soil and feed off the roots of the grasses, growing and gathering energy. Eventually the caterpillars pupate, then emerge from the soil as adults. The adults enjoy their life as fully fledged moths for only a few days, as they don't have the necessary mouthparts to feed.

WHERE TO LOOK Victoria's volcanic plains (west of Melbourne/Naarm), some areas around Melbourne itself and extending up into NSW to the ACT. They feed primarily on native grasses, often wallaby grass (*Rytidosperma* spp.) or spear grass (*Austrostipa* spp.), so look in areas where there are undisturbed native grasslands. However, there is some evidence they can also occur on patches dominated by Chilean needlegrass (*Nassella neesiana*), an introduced weed.

WHEN TO LOOK Adult moths emerge in late spring and early summer.

HABITAT HELP If you live in Australia's south-east, you can work to create pockets of native wallaby grass on your own property, or encourage local landcare groups to recognise the importance of existing areas of grassland habitat.

SIMILAR SPECIES Moths in this family – Castniidae – are broadly known as 'sun moths'. Only one sun moth genus, *Synemon*, is represented in Australia by about 40 species. Many of them have similar life habits and appearance.

Endoxyla leucomochla

ALYAWARR LANGUAGE
atnyemayt (pronounced ut-NYIM-ate), ('witchetty grub' from *Acacia kempeana*); *aylperlayt* (ail-PEARL-ate), (grub from the trunk of *Eucalyptus camaldulensis*); *apereng-ayerr* (a-PER-eng-ay-ERD-a); *ingweneng* (ing-WOON-ung).

GUMBAYNGGIRR LANGUAGE
juubarr (JOO-barr), ('first stage of tree grub, witchetty grub, edible'); *mulugurr* (MOO-loo-goorr), ('second stage, turns fat and yellow, sort of loses its skin'); *jiiginy* (JEE-giny), ('third stage, chrysalis').

WARLPIRI LANGUAGE
Ngarlkirdi (pronounced NGAHRL-keer-dee), (witchetty bush, witchetty grub from *Acacia kempeana*); *murlurrpa* (MOOR-lood-pa), (plant species, and grub from *Acacia monticola*); *puntalji* (POON-tal-jee), (plant species, and grub from *Acacia spondylophylla*); *wajarnpi* (WAH-jahn-pee), (plant species, and grub from *Acacia estrophiolata*).

YUGAMBEH LANGUAGE
jabumm (JUBBUM) ('grub').

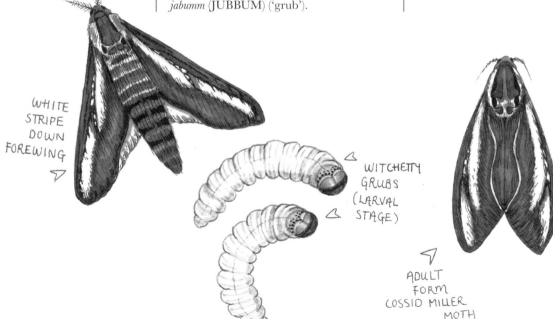

WHITE STRIPE DOWN FOREWING

WITCHETTY GRUBS (LARVAL STAGE)

ADULT FORM COSSID MILLER MOTH

WITCHETTY GRUB OR COSSID MILLER MOTH

While the majority of moths are renowned for their adult form, some moths, like the cossid miller, are much more famous for their larval form: the witchetty grub (also spelt 'witchety' or 'witjuti'). These grubs, like all moths in the family Cossidae, love to chew and bore their way into tree roots as larvae, living within the tree throughout their development, until they emerge as adults. The adult moths do not feed, and only live long enough to seek out a mate and establish the next generation.

The term 'witchetty' was not originally a name for an insect, but instead referred to the witchetty bush (*Acacia kempeana*), in which edible grubs often dwelled. The word 'witchetty' has several different spellings, and is often considered to be the name for the caterpillar of only one species: *Endoxyla leucomochla* (pictured opposite). However, First Peoples languages describe many different wood-boring grubs, using names that specify the kind of wood that the grub bores into, such as acacia, or the life stage of the insect (*see* Gumbaynggirr terms opposite). One research paper found that First Peoples across the continent consume at least 24 different species of caterpillars or grubs, showing the extent of specific cultural knowledge regarding certain species, and reaffirming that the term 'witchetty' functions as more of an umbrella name for several edible wood-boring grubs.

WHAT TO LOOK FOR Cossid moths are large grey-brown moths, with a wingspan of about 150mm. They are dark grey with a white stripe down their forewing, making them quite hard to spot against tree bark when at perch. The larvae are large white grubs, with orange-brown heads and large wood-chewing mouthparts.

LIFE CYCLE Females lay many eggs after mating, and the emerging larvae bore into nearby native trees. There, they feed and grow out of sight. When ready, the larvae tunnel close to the surface of the wood to pupate, where they can easily emerge. In some species of cossid moths, they create a little silk plug or barrier over the entry into their tree-hole to deter any disturbance while they pupate – it's like a 'do not disturb' sign of the entomology world. When ready, they emerge as adult moths to seek a mate.

WHERE TO LOOK Cossid moths can be seen sparsely throughout central and south-eastern Australia. It should be noted that identifying these species accurately can be tricky, so some moths that emerge from various native trees may be readily confused – the distribution of a single species is hard to measure. Look at night with torches in areas of native forest or mallee scrublands. As wood borers, you're unlikely to encounter larvae, but you may be able to spot damaged wattle or eucalypt trees where cockatoos have dug them out.

WHEN TO LOOK Seen sparsely in spring, summer and early autumn.

SIMILAR SPECIES Many other cossid miller moths look quite similar to this species, such as the giant wood moth (*Endoxyla cinereus*, *see* p.xxvii), found sparsely in Australia's south-east.

Multiple species in genus *Amegilla*

ALYAWARR LANGUAGE
amikw (pronounced am-EEK-wa), ('worker bee, native bee, honey fly').

YUGAMBEH LANGUAGE
kuppai (GUPP-EYE), ('native bee').

WARLPIRI LANGUAGE
Ngamardi (NGAH-mar-dee); *ngati* (NGAH-tee); *ngalypuru* (NGAHL-poo-roo), (terms for native bee).

BLUE-▽
STRIPED
ABDOMEN

▽
FINE
HAIRS OVER
BODY ▽

BLUE-BANDED BEE

For me, the sight of blue-banded bees in my garden is one of pure delight – they herald the warm months, tomatoes, flowers, and a happy garden of diverse insects. Their genus, *Amegilla* (pronounced Am-egg-ill-ah), are known as 'digger bees', as they create nesting burrows in the soil, rather than building a wax nest, or carving a burrow out of wood, like carpenter bees (*see* p.59).

Blue-banded bees are some of the few insects that perform the 'buzz pollination' that certain plants require, including many native species and some of our beloved food crops, like tomatoes. European honey bees and many of Australia's native bees cannot perform buzz pollination, but *Amegilla* bees and carpenter bees can. Blue-banded bees, after entering a flower, vibrate their flight muscles, transferring this motion up into their head, essentially 'headbanging' the pollen free of the anther. Upon flying to the next flower, they repeat the head-banging buzz, creating a chain of pollination between plants. The groovy thing is the frequency of headbanging (the one required to shake pollen from anthers) is a different frequency from that of flight. So a bee *opts* to use the buzz frequency to collect pollen. If you're very attentive when you watch one of these bees enter a flower, you can hear the pitch change between their 'flight buzz' and their 'buzz pollination'.

WHAT TO LOOK FOR A rotund bee, around 10mm long, with golden hair over the thorax, and blue and black bands across the abdomen.

LIFE CYCLE Females dig burrows in sandy soils, and make lateral tunnels where they create brood cells, and lay an egg in each. In these short tunnels they create a little lunchbox of pollen and nectar, so that when their egg hatches, the bee larvae will have the food it needs to grow and pupate, ready to one day emerge from the burrow as an adult bee. Despite being largely solitary, these bees are occasionally known to form aggregate nesting sites where multiple bees nest close together. The males, who don't take any part in nest building or brood care, rest out in the open. When darkness falls, they latch on to a plant stem with their jaws, and fold up their legs against their body to snooze.

WHERE TO LOOK Australia-wide, excluding Tasmania. These bees collect pollen and nectar from native and introduced species, so anywhere with a rich diversity of flowers is a good place to look. In my garden, they seem to love sage and chia flowers, which, like lavender, have large stalks of blue-purple flowers.

WHEN TO LOOK Year-round in the north, spring and summer in the south.

HABITAT HELP Support blue-banded bees by growing plenty of flowering native plants in your garden, including hop goodenia (*Goodenia ovata*) and flax-lilies (*Dianella* spp.). Planting groups that flower at different times can provide the bees with longer spans of time when food is abundant.

SIMILAR SPECIES European honey bees found across Australia look superficially similar, as does the buff-tailed bumble bee found in Tasmania (*see* p.202).

Thyreus caeruleopunctatus

GUMBAYNGGIRR LANGUAGE
buyuny (pronounced BOOH-yoony) (Nthn);
dungaarr (doong-gaarr) (Sthn), ('black native bee').

WARLPIRI LANGUAGE
ngarntardu (NGARN-tar-doo), ('robber bee, queen native bee').

WHITE-SPOTTED BODY

WAROONA CUCKOO BEE

CHEQUERED CUCKOO BEE

BLUE-SPOTTED BODY

CHEQUERED CUCKOO BEE

Chequered cuckoo bees remind me of Clive Owen's character from *Inside Man* (2006). These cheeky bees essentially perform a bank robbery, only this time it's a bee-bank and, like any well-executed heist, the security guards don't know until it's too late. The chequered cuckoo bee may be a thief, but it's hard not to be fascinated by their ruthless self-importance. Cloak and dagger cuckoo bees – members of the genus *Thyreus* – are usually vibrantly coloured in blue and black patterns. Unlike European honey bees, they live solitary lives, roaming and feeding with no associated hive or queen.

These bees have earned the title 'cuckoo bee', because they sneak their eggs into the nests of other bee species (such as the blue-banded bee, *see* p.55). The cuckoo bee creeps into the nest of another bee species, stealthily lays an egg there, where the poor mama bee has been industriously gathering supplies for her own egg. The cuckoo bee egg hatches before the host's eggs do, allowing the cuckoo bee grub to scoff all the resources. (Meanwhile, the parent cuckoo bee lives on, unhindered by the labours of bee rearing.) Having filched the resources out of the nest, formed a pupa, then hatched into an adult, the cuckoo bee eats its way out of the cell, leaves the nest, and begins a life of roaming and mischievous egg-laying, dazzling spectators wherever they go.

WHAT TO LOOK FOR A bee with a black body and vivid blue spots, around 15mm in length. If you see bees hovering about a blossom, try to get a closer look at them – you'll quickly be able to distinguish a cuckoo bee from a common honey bee.

LIFE CYCLE After mating, a female chequered cuckoo bee will go in search of a nest, usually preferring the nest of a digger bee species (*Amegilla* spp., such as the blue-banded bee). After laying her egg, the larvae will hatch, feed on the supplies gathered by the digger bee, pupate, then emerge from the nest as an adult.

WHERE TO LOOK Chequered cuckoo bees can be seen along the east coast of Australia from Melbourne/Naarm up to Cape York in Queensland and also west into parts of SA.

Occasionally I am lucky enough to see these bees moving through the garden in the Dandenong Ranges in the warmer months, when there are plenty of flowers. Areas of dense blooms, like a thicket of sage or lavender, heathland, or flowering eucalypt stands – especially in direct sunlight – are a good place to start looking.

WHEN TO LOOK Spring and summer.

SIMILAR SPECIES The genus *Thyreus* (the cuckoo bee genus) includes eight known species. In the case of some cuckoo bee species, including the Waroona cuckoo bee (*Thyreus waroonensis,* pictured opposite), the spots on the body are white, while others have variations on their body patterns. Other native bees can look superficially similar, including one common victim of cuckoo bees, the blue-banded bee (*see* p.55).

Xylocopa (subgenus Lestis) aerata

GUMBAYNGGIRR LANGUAGE
maymbi (pronounced MAYM-bee), ('carpenter bee').

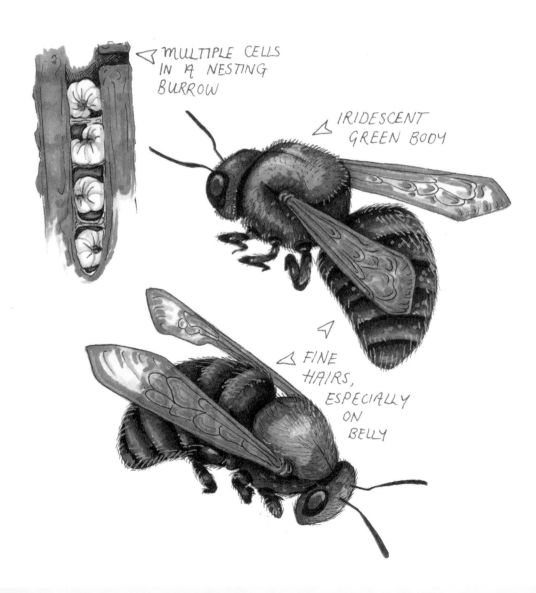

MULTIPLE CELLS IN A NESTING BURROW

IRIDESCENT GREEN BODY

FINE HAIRS, ESPECIALLY ON BELLY

GREEN CARPENTER BEE

Picture yourself on a picnic. You're near the Blue Mountains in NSW, watching dragonflies zooming over the creek, when a metallic green light catches your eye. You notice this flying jewel is, in fact, a large, vibrantly green bee, hungrily gathering pollen from flowers to take back to her nest. The name 'carpenter bee' comes from their industrious nesting habits. They carve a nesting burrow into soft woods where they lay their eggs, creating a safe space for their baby bees to develop in. Like blue-banded bees, carpenter bees are important pollinators, as they are capable of performing 'buzz pollination' (*see* p.55).

Green carpenter bees have suffered a great deal of habitat loss, and huge efforts have been made to conserve their small populations. There are only two main locations where these bees still survive: around the mountains of NSW, and on Kangaroo Island in SA. Unfortunately, both of these locations were impacted heavily by the 2019/2020 bushfires. To provide habitat and prop-up carpenter bee populations until the bush recovers, hard-working entomologists have been installing artificial nests of balsa stakes (balsa is a soft wood and mimics the density of the dead woods that green carpenter bees prefer). The ecosystem will likely take several decades to reach a point where it can adequately support green carpenter bees without aritifical intervention.

WHAT TO LOOK FOR A large (about 20mm long) bee, metallic green in colour, with fine hairs covering the body.

LIFE CYCLE A mother bee carves a nest into soft wood using specialised jaws. She then deposits a dollop of pollen as a food store, lays an egg, and constructs a little partition out of wood pulp. She repeats this pattern (another store, another egg), until she has several brood chambers set up in her wooden home. When the larvae hatch, the pollen serves as a lunchbox while they go through the early stages of growth, then pupate. Eventually – and hopefully – several adult carpenter bees will emerge from the wooden tunnel.

WHERE TO LOOK These bees once were seen across south-east SA, Victoria and in eastern NSW, however, the 2019/2020 bushfires severely diminished both their habitat and populations, making them a rare sight. They seem to prefer the dead stems of grass trees (*Xanthorrhoea*) and rotted banksia wood to build nests in. Areas of heathland on plateaus within their range are good places to look for them, if you live nearby.

WHEN TO LOOK Warm months of the year.

HABITAT HELP Encouraging the growth of mature grass trees (*Xanthorrhoea*), especially in areas of established or recovering bushland, is a great way to support this species. You can seek out local projects to contribute to directly, or you can assist any local carpenter bee populations by leaving dead branches and stems in the garden, and work to protect areas of local bushland that provide habitat to these bees.

SIMILAR SPECIES The peacock carpenter bee (*Xylocopa [Lestis] bombylans*), looks similar but has a larger and more established population, extending up along the northern NSW and Queensland coasts. *Xylocopa* is the Australian carpenter bee genus, so others of this genus group look and behave similarly.

Polistes humilis

GUMBAYNGGIRR LANGUAGE
digaarr (pronounced dee-GAARR), ('grub in paperbark, hornet, wasp').

YUGAMBEH LANGUAGE
yahwul (YAR-wool), ('wasp').

ADULT COMMON PAPER WASP

SMALL BROWN PAPER WASP NEST

BANDED ABDOMEN

PAPER WASP NEST

COMMON PAPER WASP

I imagine life inside a paper wasp nest would be aesthetically pleasing. The fractal architecture, the sunlight filtering through the shoji-style paper walls of the colony … until the worker wasps come back and start feeding dead caterpillars to their babies. Can't a wasp queen get a quiet moment of reflection around here? Not in this colony, where life is busy, and a wasp needs to work hard to gather enough resources to sustain itself, especially when there are European wasps out there to compete with.

You may have encountered small, cone-shaped hives under the gutters of your house, or in sheltered areas of your garden. These beautifully made homes are the nests of the paper wasp, a social insect that lives in a small colony. They are so-named because they collect wood, chew it and mix it with saliva to produce paper pulp. This pulp is used to build nests, usually suspended from tree branches, under awnings, and outside houses. Given humanity only invented paper about 2500 years ago (first made in China), it's pretty impressive that these little wasps have it down to such a fine art that they can live inside their paper creations. These nests (pictured opposite) are actually a group of brooding cells, a little like honeycomb in a beehive. There are a series of worker wasps, and at least one egg-laying queen (although paper wasp colonies often have more than one). Worker bees collect grubs (usually caterpillars) to carry back to the nest for the wasp larvae, providing their growing children with protein and other important nutrients. The adult wasps have such a narrow waist (called a petiole), that they cannot feed on solid food themselves, but instead subsist on flower nectar.

WHAT TO LOOK FOR These are small wasps (around 14mm long, a similar size to European honey bees). They are a rusty colour, with pale banding across the abdomen.

LIFE CYCLE Usually in late summer or autumn, drones (male wasps) are raised, then who then fly from the nest to seek out queen wasps to mate with. The newly mated queens retreat to a sheltered nook where they remain over winter, reemerging in spring to start the cycle anew. (Some build a fresh nest, others reinhabit existing nests.)

WHERE TO LOOK Paper wasps are found across Australia, but are more concentrated along the east coast and far south-west of the continent. Look in bushland reserves, scrubland and heathlands, or even around your garden. The best bet is to note any existing paper wasp nests you find, and come back to visit them as the weather warms up. It should be noted, these wasps do have stings but tend only to use them if the nest is encroached on.

WHEN TO LOOK Year-round in the north of their range, warmer months in the south of their range.

SIMILAR SPECIES There are several paper wasp species found across Australia, with relatively similar habits and appearance. One species, the small brown paper wasp (*Ropaldia revolitionalis*, pictured opposite), found in Queensland, builds paper nests in the shape of a long, descending stick.

Lissopimpla excelsa

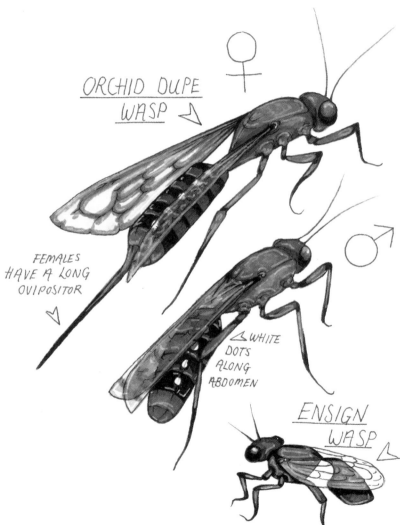

ORCHID DUPE
WASP

FEMALES
HAVE A LONG
OVIPOSITOR

WHITE
DOTS
ALONG
ABDOMEN

ENSIGN
WASP

ORCHID DUPE WASP

Seduction! Spurned lovers! Death! Deception! The fable-esque story of the orchid dupe wasp has it all. With a fire-engine red body, black tail and vicious-looking ovipositor, this wasp is certainly an unsettling-looking insect. Orchid dupe wasps are part of the Ichneumonidae family, all of whom parasitise other species of grubs. Their disturbing method of parasitising involves laying eggs in larvae of soft-bodied grubs. Yes, I said *in*. The ovipositor is 'stabbed' into the host larvae, and used to deposit an egg there. These larvae are doomed to suffer terribly after the hatching of the wasp egg, like some poor protagonist of a Grimm's fairytale. The young wasp grub hatches inside and consumes part of their host alive. Sheesh. Although this method of child-rearing is pretty nasty, parasitic wasps (of several species) are now bred up and used to control caterpillar infestations in crops. One species of parasitic wasp – *Spechophaga vesparum* – was even used to try to decrease populations of European wasps.

Though perhaps their exploitative reproduction methods are questionable, these wasps are, in turn, completely catfished by some native orchids. A group known as 'tongue orchids' (genus *Cryptostylis*), are cleverly adapted to both look and smell vaguely like a female orchid dupe wasp. The male orchid dupe wasps, who smell and see a blurry lady wasp, swoop in and try their darnedest to make a baby with that vaguely sexy waspish-orchid. The petal arrangement of the *Cryptostylis* orchids entices the male wasps into the 'embrace' of the flower to attempt to mate with it. In the process, pollen is deposited on the male was who unsuspectingly wasp heads on to the next orchid to try it all over again, ensuring the next generation of tongue orchids live on.

WHAT TO LOOK FOR A red and black wasp, about 20mm long (not including the long ovipositor of females). The body is red, and the abdomen is black with several white dots. The wings are a translucent, smoky colour (another name for this species is the dusky-winged ichneumonid).

LIFE CYCLE An adult female wasp oviposits (lays) an egg into a larval host (picture an innocent, juicy caterpillar). The egg hatches and, inside the caterpillar, the wasp larvae feeds, pupates, then emerges to seek a mate and renew the cycle. Or to go and get confused by a sexy flower.

WHERE TO LOOK This wasp is a common species in south-east and far south-west Australia, most commonly seen in wet, warm environments where lush plant life provide plenty of host species. Look in gardens and flowering bushland.

WHEN TO LOOK Spring, summer and early autumn.

SIMILAR SPECIES There are many other parasitic wasp species found in Australia, such as ensign (aka hatchet) wasps (family Evaniidae, pictured opposite), who parasitise cockroaches by preferenc. Another similar wasp is the yellow-banded ichneumon wasp (*Echthromorpha agrestoria*), which has a yellow-and-black-striped abdomen, and is found along the Queensland coast.

Sceliphron laetum

GUMBAYNGGIRR LANGUAGE
wulungarra (pronounced WOO-loo-ngah-rrah), ('wasp', 'hornet').

YUGAMBEH LANGUAGE
dugul (DOOG-ool), ('hornet').

WARLPIRI LANGUAGE
murrururruru (MOO-doo-ROO-doo-roo);
purr-muru-muru (POOD-moo-roo-moo-roo),
(terms for 'wasp', 'hornet').

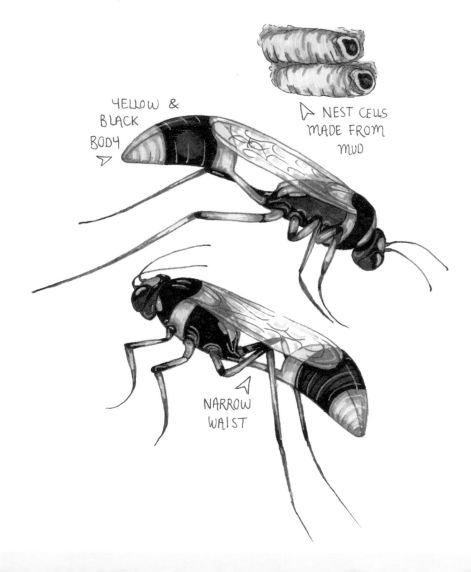

NEST CELLS MADE FROM MUD

YELLOW & BLACK BODY

NARROW WAIST

MUD-DAUBER WASP

Female mud-dauber wasps have to be one of the most diligent single parents in the insect realm. They build nests that many of us are familiar with – their tubular, clay cells are often found on house weatherboards, or in nooks and crannies around window frames. The single mother wasp carries little pellets of mud for several days, sometimes weeks, to build these brooding chambers, earning them their common name: mud-dauber.

The wasp mother-to-be provisions these individual cells with food for their soon-to-hatch baby wasps. They hunt for spiders (almost exclusively orb-weaver spiders), who they paralyse with just the right amount of venom from their stinger. This tactic ensures the spiders remain fresh for their wasp larvae, even if they remain untouched for some time. The mud-dauber wasp tends to lay only a few eggs (approximately 5–20). To give credence to the old adage 'all your eggs in one basket', the mud-dauber wasp then makes great efforts to care for and ensure the success of her young, as is illustrated by her diligent spider-hunting efforts.

WHAT TO LOOK FOR A black and yellow wasp, about 20mm long, with a very slender waist.

LIFE CYCLE After mating, a female mud-dauber wasp constructs a brooding chamber out of mud. She adds spiders to the chamber, then a single wasp egg is lain directly on to a spider. The larvae, when hatched, is then able to immediately begin feeding. Incredibly, the wasps are known to seek out certain species of spiders, which they stack in a particular order in the cells. It's theorised these clever wasps know that the softest orb-weaving spiders must be stacked closest to the larvae, while hard-exoskeleton-bearing species can be stacked for the larvae to reach when it has grown bigger. The mother repeats this process for several further cells, then 'cements' the whole thing with extra mud. After the larvae pupate, they chew their way out of their chamber to fly off as adult wasps. Sometimes these insects will go into diapause (a kind of hibernation) over winter, waiting for warmer weather before emerging.

WHERE TO LOOK Across Australia, although mud-dauber wasps are more concentrated in south-west WA and along the south and east coast of Australia. Check around your home or buildings near parklands, as adult wasps sustain themselves on flower nectar while busily building nests and catching spiders. Observing – often over a couple of days – areas around existing mud-dauber nests is worth a try. Mud-dauber wasps aren't usually aggressive, but they will use their stinger if you meddle with their nests or get in their way.

WHEN TO LOOK Most likely to be seen in spring and summer, though they may be seen more commonly throughout the year in the northern areas of their range.

SIMILAR SPECIES The fellow mud-dauber wasp (*Sceliphron formosum*) looks similar and has a similar range, and the same goes for potter wasps or Australian hornets (*Abispa ephippium*).

Oecophylla smaragdina

GUMBAYNGGIRR LANGUAGE
munygan (PRONOUNCED MOONY-gun), ('green ant').

WARLPIRI LANGUAGE
yarrkula (YAHD-koo-la), ('green ant').

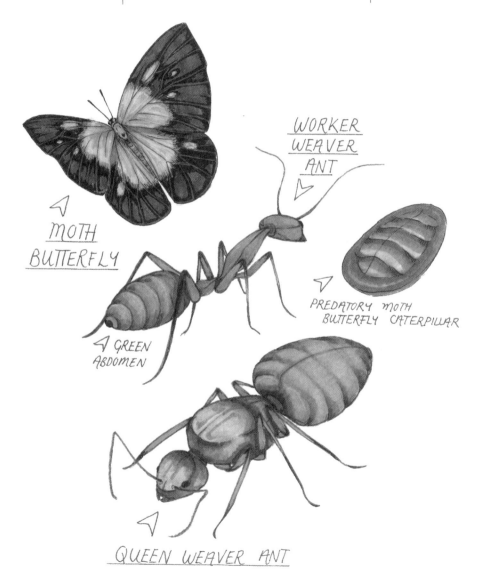

MOTH BUTTERFLY

WORKER WEAVER ANT

GREEN ABDOMEN

PREDATORY MOTH BUTTERFLY CATERPILLAR

QUEEN WEAVER ANT

WEAVER ANT

The more insects I encounter, the more I think there needs to be a *Grand Designs*: *Entomology Edition*. Like the delicate paper wasps (*see* p.61), and magnetic termites (*see* p.129), weaver ants (also called green tree ants) are visionary architects, creating homes made entirely out of leaves. Unlike many other ant species who live in sand or soil, weaver ants live in canopies amongst the leaves of trees. They create complex nests by 'sewing' leaves together (sticking the foliage together with silk). These nests become incredible systems of leafy architecture, but they can only be made through cooperation. The grubs – the larvae of ants – produce silk. While the adult ants don't make silk, they are strong. They gather along two leaf edges, stretching their little bodies out and acting like teeth on a zip, holding the leaves together. Then another set of worker ants grab themselves a grub – carefully – in their sharp mandibles, and spreads its silk along the leaf edges, gluing the leaves together. Voila! An arboreal ant nest is formed.

Weaver ants are carnivorous, mostly eating other invertebrates, and they can collaborate to eat larger prey, such as lizards or snails. In some farms, these ant colonies are encouraged as they are a natural pest control (often in cashew, mango and cocoa plantations). Some cultures enjoy preparing foods using weaver ants as an ingredient, including the Larrakia People (Darwin/Garramilla area). The ants are said to taste a bit like citrus and coriander seed. While hunters themselves, weaver ants are also prey to another fascinating insect species. The 'moth butterfly' caterpillar (*Liphyra brassolis*, pictured opposite) lives in the nests of weaver ants and feeds on their larvae and pupae. The caterpillars are heavily armoured, and unbothered by the bites of angry worker ants. The moth butterflies even pupate in the weaver nest, then emerge as adults and zoom off to renew this dastardly cycle. Carnivorous butterflies? Yes. It's a bug-eat-bug world.

WHAT TO LOOK FOR A large group of leaves bundled together with white silk, usually in the treetops, potentially with some ant activity around it. The worker ants are about 10mm long with a brownish body and a green abdomen. The queens are large, and completely green, hence the common name 'green tree ant', although I think you have to get quite lucky to see one.

LIFE CYCLE A newly raised queen ant takes a nuptial flight, during which she mates and then finds a spot in the canopy to lay eggs. She quickly loses her wings, and her first clutch of eggs hatch, grow, pupate and form her first wave of workers. The worker ants both forage for food and care for young grubs.

WHERE TO LOOK Weaver ants are found along the northern coast of Australia in WA, the NT and Queensland. If you're in those areas, look in rainforestor in orchards. It should be noted weaver ants give a painful bite, so exercise caution near their nests.

WHEN TO LOOK Year-round.

SIMILAR SPECIES These ants are pretty unmistakable, though some other insects – such as the processionary caterpillar (*see* p.37) – also create silken nests in tree canopies.

Myrmecia pilosula

ALYAWARR LANGUAGE
tyekarnparnp (pronounced CHICK-arn-parnp-a), ('jumping ant', 'bull ant', *Myrmecia* species); ntyweyapert ((i)n-CHWEE-a-pert), ('bull ant').

GUMBAYNGGIRR LANGUAGE
baln.ga-baln.ga (BULN.gah-BULN.gah), ('jumper ant'); *gumuum* (ga-MOOM), ('red ant, bull ant').

WARLPIRI LANGUAGE
pankiji (PAHN-kid-jee), ('bull ant', *Myrmecia nigriceps*).

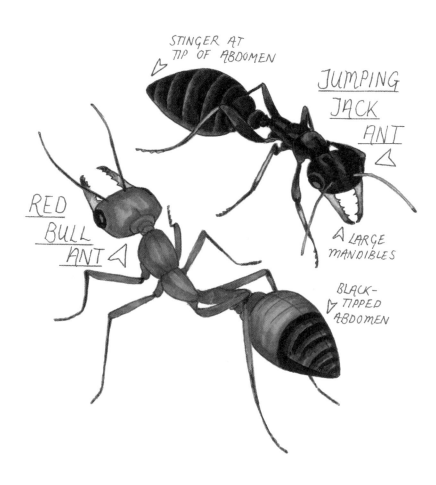

STINGER AT TIP OF ABDOMEN

JUMPING JACK ANT

RED BULL ANT

LARGE MANDIBLES

BLACK-TIPPED ABDOMEN

JUMPING JACK ANT

Australia is a continent of ants. We share the landscape with a huge amount of species and subspecies – around 1300 known so far. One of the more memorable is the jumping jack ant, to which anyone who has suffered their sting will attest. Jumping jacks tend to create nests in sandy, uncompacted soils in Australia's south-east. Earning their common name, they readily leap or hop across the soil, especially if riled up. Despite their large mandibles, the 'bite' you might get from this ant is actually delivered by a venomous stinger at the tip of their abdomen. In some people, it may cause a dangerous anaphylactic response. Jumping jacks are generalist feeders, usually pursuing sweet, easy sources of fuel, such as nectar. (The larvae have fiercer tastes, and readily consume the invertebrate prey that worker ants drag back to the nest.) The worker ants navigate visually, largely relying on landmarks to return to the nest after foraging.

Jumping jack nests are eusocial colonies (structured societies with division of labour). These societies consist of worker ants (infertile females who forage and care for larvae), the queen (who lays eggs that replenish the colony population), and fleeting generations of newly hatched queens and males who leave the nest to establish new colonies. Many different ants within *Myrmecia* may be referred to colloquially as 'jumper jack', 'jumping jack', 'bull ants' or sometimes 'bulldog ants'. Growing up, I thought of the largest of these as bull ants (those with bodies about 2cm long and huge mandibles), while the smaller, black-coloured ants that leapt and bit you unawares on a picnic were called jumping jacks.

WHAT TO LOOK FOR A black ant with yellow-orange mandibles, usually about 15mm long.

LIFE CYCLE A fertile queen lays eggs, which hatch into larvae. Worker ants care for the larvae, going out on solo foraging missions where food is sought and carried back to the colony for the larvae. These young ants will develop into new generations of workers. The individual ants you see out on a bushwalk or at the park are usually solo worker ants who are collecting supplies to carry back to the nest. Fertile male ants and fertile female queens are raised and leave the nest to establish new colonies.

WHERE TO LOOK Across Tasmania and Victoria, in east SA, and along the NSW coast. You'll spot them in parklands, bushland, walking trails, picnic areas, or any areas with sandy soils. Usually sitting quietly in an area of bushland and watching for movement across the ground will let you spot any ants crawling about.

WHEN TO LOOK Year-round, but these ants are less active in the winter months.

SIMILAR SPECIES Many of the bulldog ant(s), such as red bull ants (*Myrmercia gulosa*, pictured opposite) look similar. I reliably see these giant bull ants in sandy coastal forests and heathlands of eastern Australia.

Camponotus inflatus

ALYAWARR LANGUAGE
yerramp (pronounced YID-amp-a), ('honey ant', *Camponotus* species).

GUMBAYNGGIRR LANGUAGE
giiny (GEENY), ('ant'); *ngurlum* (NGOO-rloom), ('ant-nest').

YUGAMBEH LANGUAGE
gingging (GING-GING), ('ant').

WARLPIRI LANGUAGE
lirrakara (LID-ah-KAH-ra), ('large black honey ant').

◁ BLACK HONEY-POT ANT REPLETE

◁ ABDOMEN SWELLS WITH HONEY

BLACK HONEYPOT ANT WORKER

BANDED SUGAR ANT ▷

BLACK HONEYPOT ANT

In the arid regions of Australia where black honeypot ants live, life is harsh. Flowers bloom only for short periods of time, and are usually dependent on fickle seasonal conditions. To eke out an existence in the desert, you need to be efficient at gathering resources and storing them for the harsher times that will inevitably roll around. To navigate these difficult conditions, the black honeypot has developed an insurance policy of sorts. When conditions are right and flowers bloom in the desert, they go out foraging, and gorge themselves on flower nectar. Some of the worker ants assume an essential role by becoming the 'living larder' of the ant colony. The ants who gather nectar outside the nest will return to feed the living larder ants until their abdomen swells with honey. These honeypot ants grow so large they become immobile, and remain in chambers in the colony underground. The worker ants, when needing to refuel during times of scarcity, approach one of the honey-filled ants and tickle them using their antennae. The sugar-filled ant then regurgitates a portion of honey for the awaiting worker ant. The honey-filled ants (also known as repletes) are simply worker ants who have been randomly allocated to act as a larder for the colony – they are not biologically different from the worker ants. If a few repletes are wiped out, new worker ants can develop into these honey stores. The ants have hard exoskeletal plates that make up their abdomen, but are connected by a soft membrane which allows the hard abdominal plates to separate as the abdomen fills with honey. Nearly half of the ants of a colony can be repletes at any one time, existing purely to feed the mobile workers. That's a pretty inventive way to manage resources.

Some First Peoples across Australia's arid regions harvest replete honey ants, whose abdomens can be eaten. Though they are a particularly sweet treat, some repletes dwell nearly 2m underground, which is a *lot* of digging for a spoonful of honey.

WHAT TO LOOK FOR Worker ants are black and grow to about 15mm long. The repletes are immobile, usually in deep underground chambers. They have the same front two-thirds as the worker ants, but their abdomen has swelled to about 10–15mm across, filled with honey.

LIFE CYCLE A colony of honeypot ants is sustained by one or more fertile queens who lay eggs. Worker ants tend to the larvae, care for repletes and gather resources for the colony.

WHERE TO LOOK These ants live in the arid central regions of Australia, with fairly irregular densities over that territory. Like most other ants, they build their nests in sandy, dry soils, and worker ants will be active around the nest. Black honeypot ant colonies are often built close to mulga trees (*Acacia aneura*), which provide some shelter and access to insect prey and nectar, and are sometimes colonised by honeydew-producing lerps. The lerps provide further sugar for the ants to harvest (*see* p.201). Honey ants are of cultural significance to certain First Peoples, so please do not dig or disturb them.

SIMILAR SPECIES Superficially many ants look similar, but occupy different ecosystems to the black honeypot ant. A much more commonly seen ant in backyards and parklands is the banded sugar ant (*Camponotus consobrinus*, pictured opposite).

Perga affinis

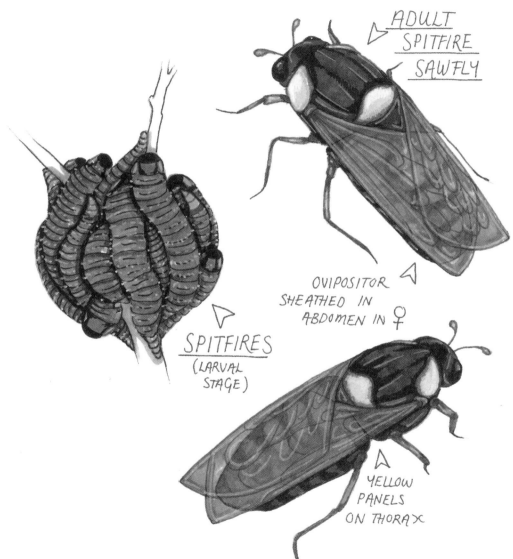

▷ ADULT
SPITFIRE
SAWFLY

OVIPOSITOR
SHEATHED IN
ABDOMEN IN ♀

▷ SPITFIRES
(LARVAL
STAGE)

YELLOW
PANELS
ON THORAX

SPITFIRE SAWFLY

As a kid, my main encounter with sawflies was with their larvae – spitfires – which my sister and I would often find in large, fascinatingly gross clumps on the branches of young trees. I remember these hairy clumps would rear up at the same time, and ooze a yucky fluid. Perfect fodder for a kid's curiosity. (I collected several of them in an ice-cream tub one day, but I think I forgot about them and they escaped across the verandah and back into the garden.) The larvae feed on leaves at night, and in the daylight hours they group together in clumps, which is likely an attempt to discourage predators. These grubs, of course, are only one stage of the sawfly life cycle.

Although their colloquial name is 'sawfly', spitfire sawflies are not a member of the fly order (Diptera, *see* pp.xiv, 155), but are of the same order as bees, wasps and ants (Hymenoptera). They aren't especially fly or bee-like in behaviour – as adults, they live singly and survive only a matter of days. But what I really want to tell you about is the origin of the name 'sawfly'. It comes from the fierce female sawflies, who each have a specially modified ovipositor that unfolds out of their abdomen, and is serrated like a tiny saw. They use this to saw into wood, into which they lay their eggs. Sawflies: the pocket-knives of the insect world.

WHAT TO LOOK FOR Spitfires (sawfly larvae) look kind of like black caterpillars covered with white hairs, and have an orange-yellow tip to their abdomen. The adult sawflies are about 20mm long, dark coloured, and have a large yellow dot on the centre of their back and on each shoulder. They look initially a bit like a cross between a wasp and a bee, but chunkier.

LIFE CYCLE Female sawflies lay their eggs in a cut they make in a tree using their serrated ovipositor. The eggs hatch, the larvae emerge and congregate to feed for about six months, until they are ready to pupate in the soil. The adults then emerge to mate and renew the cycle.

WHERE TO LOOK Across the southern half of the continent, including Tasmania, although they are much more common in the thickly vegetated areas of the south-east of mainland Australia and south-west WA. Look in local gardens and parklands, and especially keep your eyes out for groups of dark grubs all clumped together on tree stems or leaves. If you're lucky, you might see adult sawflies out and about in local heathlands or bushland, but I seem to have more luck seeing them at their larval stage.

WHEN TO LOOK Spitfire sawfly adults are usually seen in spring and summer, but may persist year-round in warmer northern climates.

HABITAT HELP Retaining areas of native bushland is a good start, and planting further native trees, especially eucalypt, can encourage the success of sawfly species.

SIMILAR SPECIES There are over 100 species of sawfly in Australia (family Pergidae). Another common species of sawfly, the bottlebrush sawfly (*Pterygophorus cinctus*) has different looking larvae, but relatively similar looking adults. The slimy cherry or pear slugs (*Caliroa cerasi*) that sometimes damage fruit trees are a larval stage of another sawfly.

Chrysolopus spectabilis

WARLPIRI LANGUAGE
lukarrara (pronounced LUKE-ah-DA-ra),
('weevil-nosed beetle').

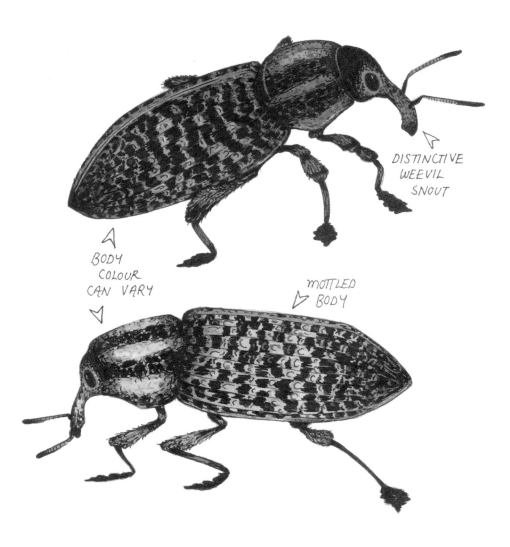

DISTINCTIVE
WEEVIL
SNOUT

BODY
COLOUR
CAN VARY

MOTTLED
BODY

BOTANY BAY WEEVIL

These slow-moving, large-eyed, long-nosed beetles are well renowned amongst insect collectors, as the Botany Bay weevil was one of the first Australian insects to be described by Western science. These beetles, also known as the diamond weevil, munches on wattle roots in its larval stage, and on wattle leaves as an adult. Although they can fly, they seem to prefer slowly lumbering amongst foliage. If disturbed, they play dead, meaning they freeze and drop off their perch to try to avoid attack (a strategy known as 'thanatosis'). They also have particularly large eyes, so they look a little imploring as they cruise around. Something about their shyness, big eyes, and long snout lends them an endearing Eeyore-esque quality (from *Winnie-the-Pooh*), as if they're always a little bit melancholy. The Botany Bay weevil is part of the 'true' weevil family (Curculionidae), who all have adorable snouts and elbow-like joints in their antennae.

I should clarify that Botany Bay weevils are different from the weevils that get into your flour at home. Some pantry pests *are* weevils, such as the rice weevil (*Sitophilus oryzae*), but the most common ones are actually moths, most often the Indian meal moth (*Plodia interpunctella*). They lay their eggs in flour and grain, where the resultant grubs thrive, leaving sticky webs in their wake.

WHAT TO LOOK FOR A large (15–20mm long), black-and-blue patterned beetle with cute golf-club feet, and a long snout. The females are significantly larger than the males, though this will be hard to perceive unless you see two close to one another. I have heard of people seeing more greenish-patterned weevils (rather than blue), so there must be some regional and/or seasonal variation in colour. At the Australian National Insect Collection on Ngunnawal Country in Canberra/Ngambri/Ngunnawal, the Botany Bay weevil display shows an amazing diversity of blues, greens and yellows.

LIFE CYCLE Using their industrious little snouts, adult female weevils drill holes into the base of plants into which they lay their eggs (commonly in wattle trees). The eggs hatch into larvae who subsist off the plant roots. The larvae, when ready, pupate and then emerge as adult beetles.

WHERE TO LOOK These beetles can be found in south-east SA, across Victoria and NSW, and in eastern Queensland. They use their long snout to feed on foliage and softer stems, especially acacias, so look in lush bush reserves or parklands where there are plenty of wattles.

WHEN TO LOOK Spring and summer.

SIMILAR SPECIES The 'true' weevil family is Curculionidae, and there are many weevils recognised in Australia – nearly 6500 species. Many of these species have a recognisably long snout and rounded body, with similar feeding habits. For example, the group of weevils known as wattle pigs (genus *Leptopius*) look similar, though they tend to be pale brown, and are seen across Australia.

Hoshihananomia leucosticta

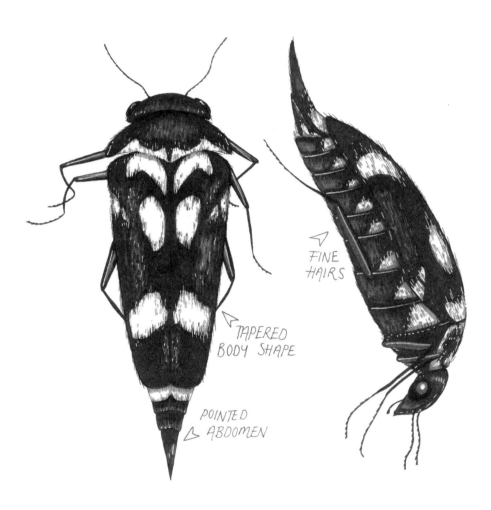

TAPERED
BODY SHAPE

POINTED
ABDOMEN

FINE
HAIRS

WHITE-SPOTTED PINTAIL BEETLE

The white-spotted pintail beetle is a member of a particularly cute and acrobatic family of insects, known as the tumbling flower beetles (family Mordellidae). These delicate beetles have a pretty anxious energy, moving quickly through blossoms, feeding on nectar, pausing only occasionally to soak up sun on exposed flowers. When disturbed they throw themselves into a series of twisty hops to evade capture, hence the name: 'tumbling flower beetles'. These critters are worthy of entry to Cirque du Soleil, powering their jumps using their strong hind legs, which they use to launch themselves out of harm's way. They can also fly, so they have multiple options for escape.

The distinctive body shape of the white-spotted pintail beetle makes them easy to identify – look for a tapered body that comes to a sharp point at the end of the abdomen (don't worry, it's not a stinger). This peculiar shape can, at first glance, make them look a little waspish, but with inspection you'll be able to see their hardened elytra and recognise them as beetles. They frequent flowers to eat nectar and, as a result, are probably effective pollinators. There are about 100 known species of tumbling flower beetles in Australia. The white-spotted pintail beetle likely bores into decaying wood as larvae, while some other pintail beetles bore into living plant stems to feed on, while others parasitise other insect larvae.

WHAT TO LOOK FOR A small (about 10mm long) beetle, black with white spots, with a wide thorax and a body that tapers to a sharp point at the tip of their abdomen. Their elytra (wing covers) do not fully cover their body, leaving the pointed abdomen tip exposed. They also have cute little antennae, kept partially out of sight under their shyly bent heads. Their underbellies are patterned with black and white stripes.

LIFE CYCLE Female pintail beetles lay eggs in decaying wood, so the larvae have something to feed on immediately after hatching. The larvae feed and grow *in situ*, until they pupate and emerge as adults in the warmer months.

WHERE TO LOOK In south-east SA, Victoria, Tasmania, NSW and south-east Queensland. Look amongst the flowers of eucalypts, tea trees, or other natives. Areas where there are nectar-rich flowers are the best bet, especially in lush gardens or forest areas.

WHEN TO LOOK Late spring and summer.

SIMILAR SPECIES There are several species of pintail beetle in Australia, such as the tiny black pintail beetle (*Tomoxioda aterrima*) in eastern Australia, or another south-east Australian pintail beetle (*Mordella sydneyana*), which looks much like the white-spotted pintail beetle, only greyer.

Eupoecila australasiae

WARLPIRI LANGUAGE
lantipi (pronounced LAHN-tih-pee),
('flying beetle').

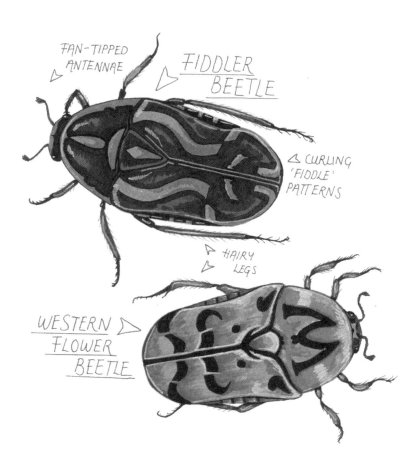

FAN-TIPPED ANTENNAE

FIDDLER BEETLE

CURLING 'FIDDLE' PATTERNS

HAIRY LEGS

WESTERN FLOWER BEETLE

FIDDLER BEETLE

Fiddler beetles are named for the vivid green patterns on their carapace, which are similar in shape to the openings on a violin. The beetles are about the size of your thumbnail, or slightly bigger, and are usually seen crawling around in gardens during the day, either lapping up nectar, or buzzing their way between flowers. They particularly love native inflorescences (clustered flowers), such as banksias or thickly flowering gum trees (the botanical equivalent of a bottomless buffet). They have functional wings, reminiscent of Christmas beetles (*see* p.85), but tend to be a bit clunky and bumbling in flight, adding to their endearing quality. Along with many other flower beetles (*see* p.81), dung beetles (*see* p.89), and Christmas beetles, the fiddler beetle is part of the family Scarabaeidae.

Scarab beetles aren't just the (fictional) flesh-eating scarabs you've see in *The Mummy* (1999), but are a diverse group of often very beautiful beetles. The majority of scarabs are colourful, gentle creatures that would prefer to be left alone so they can continue drinking nectar and sunbaking, thank you very much. Members of this family are characterised by antennae that have a little fan at their tip (known as 'lamellate' antennae) and a larval stage that is a c-shaped grub that dwells in the soil. You'll encounter several more varieties of scarab beetles in this book (*see* p.81–91). Fiddler beetles are a particularly spectacular example.

WHAT TO LOOK FOR A large, shiny black and green beetle (about 15–20mm long) with red legs. The larvae are white, c-shaped grubs that you might see in the soil in your garden.

LIFE CYCLE Adult female fiddler beetles lay eggs in decomposing wood or soil. The eggs hatch, and the grubs live underground, and feed off decomposing wood. When well fed, the grubs pupate in the soil, and then emerge in the warmer months as adults.

WHERE TO LOOK Along Australia's east coast, from south-east SA to about the Cairns area in northern Queensland. These insects love nectar, so the best bet is to head to flowering heathland or bush, such as banksia forest or areas with flowering eucalypts.

WHEN TO LOOK Spring and summer.

HABITAT HELP Leaving remnant decomposing wood in your garden can provide habitat, not only to fiddler beetles but to a great variety of local decomposer species. You can support adult fiddler beetles by growing nectar-rich, flowering native plants, like banksias or eucalypts.

SIMILAR SPECIES Many other members of the scarab family have vivid colours and a similar body shape. The flower beetle (*Eupoecila inscripta*, pictured opposite) also has beautiful green and black patterning and is found in WA.

Neorrhina punctata

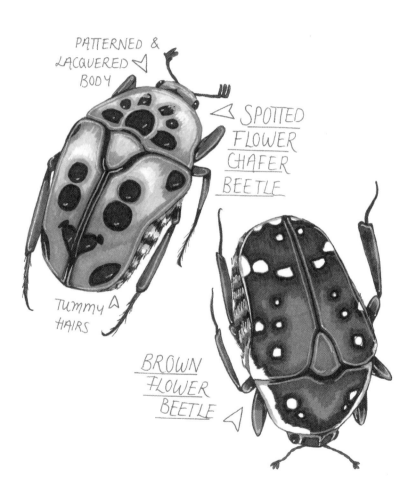

PATTERNED &
LACQUERED
BODY

SPOTTED
FLOWER
CHAFER
BEETLE

TUMMY
HAIRS

BROWN
FLOWER
BEETLE

SPOTTED FLOWER CHAFER BEETLE

One grey afternoon, I was walking along the shore of an inlet when I spotted something perched on a piece of driftwood in the shallows. Getting closer, I saw, to my delight, that it was a small scarab beetle, patterned with black polka dots. This little beetle was supremely put-together, complete with a leopard-print outfit and a fur-lined belly, like a veritable Miranda Priestly from the film *The Devil Wears Prada* (2006). I had seen photos of these marvellous beetles before, but this was the first time I'd ever seen one in the flesh. I promptly moved it onshore into the shrubs where hopefully it could seek out some nectar to sustain itself.

Like many others in the flower chafer beetle group (subfamily Cetoniinae, part of the scarab family), spotted flower chafer beetles have gloriously lacquered-looking elytra (wing covers). They love to explore flower florets where they readily subsist on pollen and nectar, especially from gum trees and tea trees. Their fabulous tummy hairs unwittingly assist in picking up and transporting pollen between flowers while they feed, so these little beetles also provide some pollination services. After a season with decent rainfall, there may be a short flush of spotted flower chafer beetles around, and then their numbers quickly diminish again.

WHAT TO LOOK FOR A shiny, golden-beige coloured beetle with black polka dots, about 15mm long. These beetles have pinkish legs and fine, light hairs on their underbelly.

LIFE CYCLE Adult female spotted flower chafers lay eggs in soil. The eggs hatch, and the larvae feed on decaying wood and other organic matter in the soil. They also pupate underground. As adults, they wriggle to the surface in warmer months to fly, mate, and flaunt their fabulous polka dot outfits.

WHERE TO LOOK Along Australia's east coast from Cape York in far-north Queensland to western Victoria, though their numbers fluctuate season to season, depending on conditions. Adult chafer beetles love to crawl on and in native flowers and fly between them, where they feed on the nectar and pollen. Try any areas of bushland rich in tea-trees, banksias and eucalypt trees.

WHEN TO LOOK Late spring and summer. Adults commonly emerge in summer after rain has softened the soils.

SIMILAR SPECIES Many other members of the flower chafer subfamily (Cetoniinae) and, more broadly, the scarab group, look similar to the spotted flower chafer, including the washerwoman Christmas beetle (*see* p.85), and the cowboy beetle (*see* p.83). Many other flower chafers have beautiful patterns and colouring, such as the brown flower beetle (*Glycyphana stolata*, pictured opposite), which has a similar distribution to the spotted flower chafer.

Chondropyga dorsalis

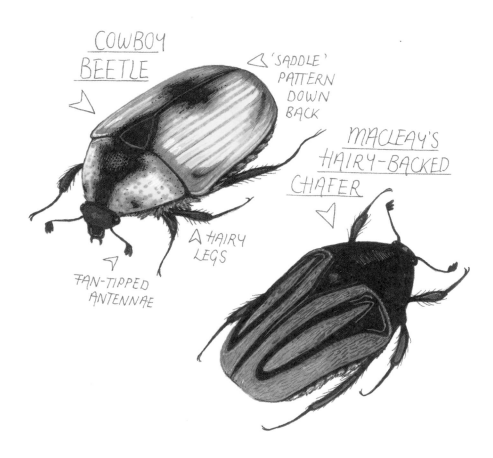

COWBOY
BEETLE

'SADDLE'
PATTERN
DOWN
BACK

MACLEAY'S
HAIRY-BACKED
CHAFER

HAIRY
LEGS

FAN-TIPPED
ANTENNAE

COWBOY BEETLE

With their antler-like antennae, hairy legs and underbelly, and suede jacket colour-scheme, cowboy beetles could readily be pictured galloping across the frontier deserts, complete with chaps and tasselled jackets. In reality, these handsome beetles tend to roam around in lush gardens during daylight hours, where they feed and seek a mate. Cowboy beetles make a loud buzzing noise when they fly which, given their size, may initially be a little disconcerting (don't worry though – the worst they can do is clumsily fly into you). Their fine tummy hairs – like the other flower chafers – likely provide some pollination services to the plants they feed from.

Occasionally certain larvae from this subfamily, Cetoniinae, will feed off plant roots, causing stunted growth in plants, hence the common name 'flower chafer' (*see* p.81).

WHAT TO LOOK FOR These beetles are large (about 25mm long) and look superficially like a Christmas beetle. Their wing covers are a brownish-tan colour with a black saddle-esque pattern down their back. They also have two 'horns' (actually antennae), adding to their Wild West aesthetic. Some of them have fairly long hair down their legs, making them look like they're wearing fringed chaps – like a true wrangler. Their larvae are white c-shaped grubs.

LIFE CYCLE Cowboy beetles lay their eggs in the soil, ideally near to good sources of decaying vegetative matter or directly in decomposing wood. The larvae hatch and feed, contributing to essential nutrient recycling in our gardens and parklands. Flower chafers are one of many insects that help make our soils lush. When well-fed, the larvae pupate to eventually emerge from the soil as adults in the warmer months.

WHERE TO LOOK Along Australia's east coast in Victoria, NSW and Queensland. The adult cowboy beetles live off nectar and pollen, so any lush, nectar-rich flowering garden is a potential happy place for them to live in. They are also successful in native bushland, often feeding from the flowers of tea trees or eucalypt trees.

WHEN TO LOOK Late spring and summer.

SIMILAR SPECIES Many of the scarab family beetles are similar in body shape to one another, such as the spotted flower chafer (*see* p.81), fiddler beetle (*see* p.79), and washerwoman Christmas beetle (*see* p.85). Hopefully you'll notice many species of flower chafer beetles in your local area, not only the cowboy beetle. Macleay's hairy-backed chafer (*Trichaulax macleayi*, pictured opposite), also about 25mm long, is found in tropical north Queensland.

Anoplognathus porosus

SHINY GOLDEN CARAPACE

LARVAL STAGE

ADULT WASHERWOMAN CHRISTMAS BEETLE

FAN-TIPPED ANTENNAE

WASHERWOMAN CHRISTMAS BEETLE

Though associated by name with Christmas traditions, these gloriously shiny beetles have always been a symbol of both seasonal and annual change, regardless of what end-of-year ritual was happening. As a kid, I would often gently lift green, copper and gold Christmas beetles off the ledge outside the kitchen window, where they gathered thickly at night, drawn towards the light. When you had one on your hand you could look closely at their amazing colour, and their spectacular, armoured anatomy. I think for many people growing up in Australia, when the Christmas beetles started gathering on the verandah light, you knew that summer had arrived. Perhaps one of the most readily recognised of the Christmas beetles is the washerwoman Christmas beetle. A common visitor to gardens, verandahs, flyscreens, kitchens, lawns and trees, these golden beetles arrive in the hot summer months and feed on eucalypt leaves, flying clumsily and briefly between destinations.

In earlier decades, Christmas beetles, the washerwoman included, were considered significant pests due to their high consumption of leaves, sometimes defoliating plantation trees. However, most likely due to habitat loss, Christmas beetles have become a rarer sight. I have referred to *A. porusus* as the 'washerwoman Christmas beetle' but, due to a fair bit of pattern and colour variation, *Anoplognathus* species beetles are readily confused for one another, and thus often have multiple – or shared – common names.

WHAT TO LOOK FOR A big, shiny, golden beetle, about 20mm long. They have tiny branched antennae, like minute deer antlers (adorable). The larvae are white, horseshoe-shaped grubs that hang out in the soil.

LIFE CYCLE Adult female Christmas beetles lay eggs in the soil. The larvae wriggle their way to nearby root masses to feed on them. They pupate under the soil, then emerge as shining adult beetles, often crawling dazedly across grass lawns for a while before taking flight.

WHERE TO LOOK The washerwoman Christmas beetle can be seen along Australia's east coast, excluding Tasmania. They rely on eucalypt trees as adults, and usually are more numerous after a season of decent rain, though their populations seem to fluctuate a lot year to year. The adult beetles are drawn to lights, so they may congregate around your house on summer nights. Some of my best Christmas beetle encounters have, strangely enough, been when visiting communal buildings at parks or in campgrounds, and seeing a huge array of beetles and other insects drawn to the fluorescent light.

WHEN TO LOOK Late spring and summer.

SIMILAR SPECIES There are about 35 species of Christmas beetles in Australia, mostly within the *Anoplognathus* genus. Most are an orange, gold, yellow or green colour with similar body shapes. One cute example is the granny smith beetle (*Anoplognathus prasinus*), found along the southern Queensland and NSW coast.

Multiple species in genus Phyllotocus

ALYAWARR LANGUAGE
anaty-anaty (pronounced a-NAITCH-a-naitch), ('type of beetle').

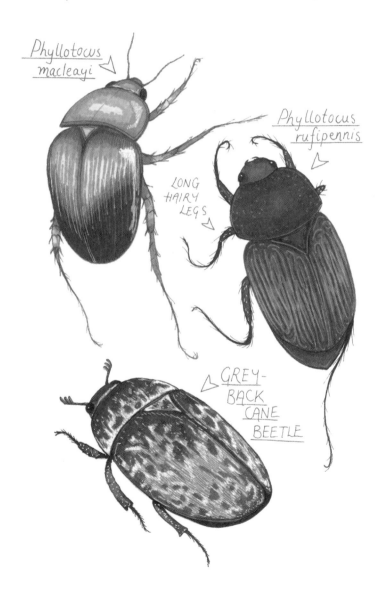

Phyllotocus macleayi ▷

Phyllotocus rufipennis ▷

LONG HAIRY LEGS ▷

▷ GREY-BACK CANE BEETLE

NECTAR SCARAB BEETLE

These little beetles will be a common sight to many readers, as they often congregate about porch lights and on fly screens in summertime, much like their close relatives: Christmas beetles (*see* p.85). Nectar scarab beetles have hairy, spiky legs, and are endearingly clumsy in both flight and while crawling. Like some other scarabs (*see* p.81), they tend to drag and shift pollen between flowers, thus providing some unwitting pollination services in flowering species. Also like the flower chafers, nectar scarabs are largely diurnal, seeking out food during hours of sunshine. Sometimes at night, they can be found hiding under flowers, as if they were too scared to leave their beloved source of nectar. As larvae, nectar scarabs live underground, likely feeding on roots, organic matter, or a combination of both.

WHAT TO LOOK FOR Small, orange-brown beetles, about 5mm long, often with some areas of black patterning. The soil-dwelling larvae are white horseshoe-shaped grubs.

LIFE CYCLE After mating, female nectar scarabs lay eggs in the soil. The eggs hatch and the larvae burrow underground, where they feed on organic matter until they are ready to pupate.

WHERE TO LOOK There are many kinds of nectar scarab beetles, most of them concentrated in Australia's south-east (south-east SA, south-east Queensland, eastern NSW, and across Victoria and Tasmania). Adult flower chafers love nectar, so head to areas of flowering heathlands, parklands and botanic gardens. Scan shrubs where there are clusters of flowers, and check around the outside of your home at night as these beetles are drawn to light on windows. (The other night, one woke me up when it clumsily flew into my forehead.)

WHEN TO LOOK Spring and summer, when there are plenty of flowers and warm weather. The adult beetles often emerge from the ground after rain, when the soil is soft and easy to burrow through.

SIMILAR SPECIES The nectar scarabs are all quite similar in appearance, so you will hopefully be able to recognise them as the small, copper, flower-loving beetles they are. Two common nectar scarab beetles are *Phyllotocus rufipennis* (pictured opposite) and *Phyllotocus macleayi* (pictured opposite), both found in south-east Australia, including Tasmania. Another scarab, the greyback cane beetle (*Dermolepida albohirtum*, pictured opposite), is also similar, though with different colouring. This cane beetle is a pest of sugarcane plantations in Australia's north. Back in the 1930s, the mysterious Bureau of Sugar Experiment Stations (yes, that was their real name) decided to introduce a certain poisonous toad species to control the numbers of cane beetles in commercial crops. As it turns out, cane toads don't even really eat the cane beetles as hoped. Instead, the toads have a rapidly spreading frontier and probably will be running the country by 2030.

Onthophagus pentacanthus

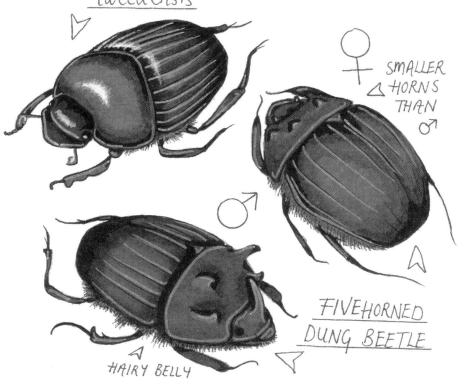

Onthophagus
tweedensis

♀ SMALLER
HORNS
THAN
♂

♂

FIVEHORNED
DUNG BEETLE

HAIRY BELLY

FIVE HORNED DUNG BEETLE

I know dung, at a conceptual level, is gross, but trust me, the stuff is pretty important. Besides, how can you overlook these little cuties, despite their off-putting name and habits? The five horned dung beetle, as you may have guessed, eats poop (the classy scientific term being 'coprophagous'). The beetle provisions dung in underground tunnels for their larvae. While there are many native dung beetles in Australia, there are about 30 established species of introduced dung beetles, brought in by the CSIRO, starting back in the 1960s. These imported beetles assist in recycling and reducing agricultural waste (read: cow manure) from building up to excess. Without beginning to inspect introduced species, there are *plenty* of native dung beetle species to learn about (roughly 500), such as the five horned dung beetle. Much more study is needed to understand their role in Australian environments, although we do know they are specialists in working with marsupial poop (such as that of wombats, kangaroos or wallabies). As a result, dung beetles play an important role in non-agricultural systems, recycling nutrients, and bioturbation (turning over soils). They also sometimes vary their diet and consume decaying organic matter, fungi or fruit, or provision these substances for their unhatched larvae.

Dung beetles have been revered in many different cultures. In Ancient Egypt, it was believed that dung beetles rolled dung in the same manner the god Khepri rolled the sun across the sky each day. Some beetles bear the genus name *Sisyphus*, after the Ancient Greek myth of Sisyphus who was doomed to eternally push a boulder up a mountain. I propose we too should revere dung beetles for their contributions to ecosystems, in all their coprophagous glory.

WHAT TO LOOK FOR A dark brown-black scarab beetle, about 15mm long, with five horns over the 'forehead', and rusty fringe of hair on the underbelly.

LIFE CYCLE After mating, female dung beetles will tunnel burrows into the ground, and stock these with dung, creating little 'tuckerboxes' to fuel their larvae as they develop. After the larvae feed, grow and pupate underground, the adult beetles emerge to tango with more dung and renew the cycle.

WHERE TO LOOK Across south-east SA, western Vic and in NSW, mirroring the Murray–Darling basin. Many other native species of dung beetles can be seen across the continent, including Tasmania. These beetles are nocturnal, so keep an eye out for them on an evening stroll with a head torch, especially in arid bushland areas.

WHEN TO LOOK Year-round.

HABITAT HELP Protecting areas of native bush reserve, especially parks that sustain populations of mammals, also protects Australian dung beetles.

SIMILAR SPECIES Many other species of both native and introduced dung beetles have a similar appearance, such as the native green dung beetle (*Onthophagus tweedensis*, pictured opposite), found in south-east Queensland and north-east NSW. Some of these amazing beetles are so keen for fresh dung, they have developed specialised prehensile claws to assist their poop-pursuits. Using these claws, beetles actually cling to the fur around the backside of an animal, and latch on to the dung as it is, *ahem*, expelled. The early bird gets the worm, I suppose.

Xylotrupes gideon (subspecies *australicus*)

WARLPIRI LANGUAGE
miji-miji (pronounced MIH-jee-MIH-jee);
purrurdujinpa (POOR-doo-doo-jin-pah),
(terms for 'brown dynastine beetle',
'rhinoceros beetle').

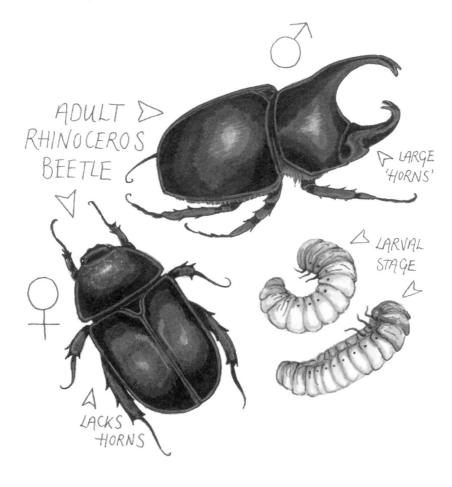

ADULT ▷
RHINOCEROS
BEETLE

LARGE
'HORNS'

LARVAL
STAGE

LACKS
HORNS

RHINOCEROS BEETLE

Male rhinoceros beetles have huge horns that they use to vie with other males in competition for a mate – hence the name 'rhinoceros beetle'. (Meanwhile, the female rhinoceros beetles seem to just mellowly drink tree sap and amicably live their little beetle lives without too much conflict.) Despite their competition for love, they are generally pretty slow-moving beetles that like to hang out in tree canopies or on branches where they can feed and seek a mate. Like the golden stag beetle (*see* p.93), rhinoceros beetles sometimes feed at the broken-off young shoots of trees, likely drinking sap flowing from these wounds. That said, they've been reported to feed on various fruits, bark, young shoots and leaves on trees, so it perhaps depends on food availability in a given season. The adult beetles are often drawn to light, so if you live within their range you may be lucky enough to see some congregating in your garden at night.

The Australian rhinoceros beetle is part of the scarab group, alongside Christmas beetles (*see* p.85), dung beetles (*see* p.89) and stag beetles (*see* p.93). This species, *Xylotrupes gideon*, has sixteen species across Southeast Asia, but *Xylotrupes gideon australicus* is the only representative found in Australia, making it quite a special sighting. It's discoveries like this that make me feel even more privileged to live in Australia. These beetles are also sometimes referred to as elephant beetles.

WHAT TO LOOK FOR A shiny brown-black beetle, about 40mm long, with two huge, pincer-like horns. If you look closely, you'll see the horns are 'forked' at their tip (they're really quite artful, given they're weapons of romantic competition). That said, only the males possess the horns, while the females have a smooth thorax and head, and are a bit smaller than males.

LIFE CYCLE Adult female rhinoceros beetles tend to lay eggs amongst mulch or leaf litter. The grubs hatch and feed on organic matter, growing and creating a little hollow for themselves in the soil where they pupate. When ready, an adult rhinoceros beetle will emerge from the soil to seek food and a mate.

WHERE TO LOOK These beetles can be seen from the northern Queensland coast down into Eora Country (near Sydney/Warrang) in NSW. They seem to prefer native forest environments, though they may sometimes venture into suburban gardens, as they readily feed on introduced trees. Look in bushland reserves, rainforest areas or botanic gardens.

WHEN TO LOOK Late spring and summer.

SIMILAR SPECIES Other beetles in the subfamily Dynastinae are also known as 'rhinoceros beetles', though few are as spectacular as the rhinoceros beetle. Another example is the more modest rhinoceros beetle (*Haploscapanes barbarossa*), found sparsely across the northern half of Australia.

Lamprima aurata

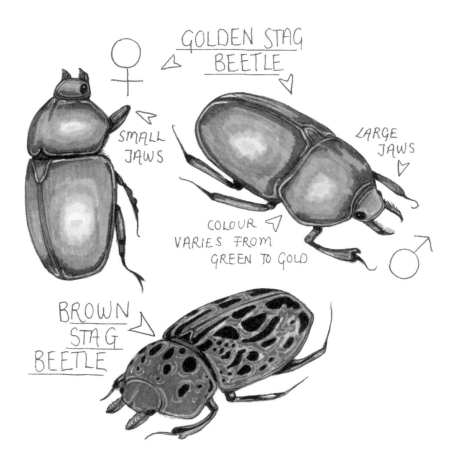

GOLDEN STAG BEETLE

♀

SMALL JAWS

LARGE JAWS

COLOUR VARIES FROM GREEN TO GOLD

♂

BROWN STAG BEETLE

GOLDEN STAG BEETLE

Defenestration: the act of throwing someone out of a window. I hadn't expected to use this wonderfully evocative word in reference to Australian insects, but here we are. Allow me to introduce the golden stag beetle who, in regal metallic hues, is easy to imagine as a tiny armour-wearing knight, doing their duty to protect the (beetle) realm. There are actually multiple Australian scarabs colloquially called 'golden stag beetles', each species occupying different areas across the continent, but they all have relatively similar life habits. These striking beetles thus are fairly widespread, but not particularly common, so they always make for a delightful sight.

As young grubs, golden stag beetles feed on tree root networks, and pupate under the soil, taking at least two years to develop into adults. After emerging, they usually fly up into tree canopies, where the male beetles use their large mandibles to snip off the tip of a young tree shoot. From the cut stem, they feed on the tree sap, sharing it with female beetles. The male stag beetles, knights-of-the-realm-style, defend their sap-flows rather vigorously. Here, my friends, we arrive at defenestration: if two males begin to fight over a stem, the larger male will usually deal with the smaller by lifting him up in his jaws, then throwing him out of the tree. There you have it: stag beetles daily re-enact the infamous 1600s Prague defenestrations, where several governors were thrown from windows. Incredible.

WHAT TO LOOK FOR A metallic green beetle (about 15–20mm long). The male beetles have large forward-jutting jaws, while the females have much smaller mandibles. Like Christmas beetles (*see* p.85), they have shiny metallic carapaces. The golden stag beetle can have a great degree of colour and size variation, depending on seasonal conditions, so you may see green, yellow-gold, rusty-orange, or bronze-coloured beetles. The larvae are white soil-dwelling grubs.

LIFE CYCLE Female stag beetles lay eggs in short tunnels in the soil, or in very soft decomposed wood. The emerging larvae feed on roots, growing until they are ready to pupate under the soil. After pupating, they emerge as fully-fledged adult beetles, ready to seek out a mate, drink sap and toss foes.

WHERE TO LOOK The golden stag beetle can be seen in south-west WA, south-east SA, across Victoria, Tasmania, and along the NSW and Queensland coastline. These beetles rely on native trees and loamy soil, so head to bushland reserves, parks, botanic gardens or look carefully through suburban gardens adjacent to bushland. Golden stag beetles have been observed feeding sometimes on fruit and nectar, but they mostly habituate tree canopies where the foliage is much more effective for beetle-slinging.

WHEN TO LOOK Spring and summer.

SIMILAR SPECIES Other species of the *Laprima* genus are the spectacular and huge Mueller's stag beetle (*Phalacrognathus muelleri*), found on the north Queensland coast; or the brown stag beetle (*Ryssonotus nebulosus,* pictured opposite), found along the east coast of mainland Australia.

Family Chrysomelidae

ALYAWARR LANGUAGE

antyey-iylpey-angker (pronounced an-JEE-eeyl-pee-ANG-ker-a), ('beetle')

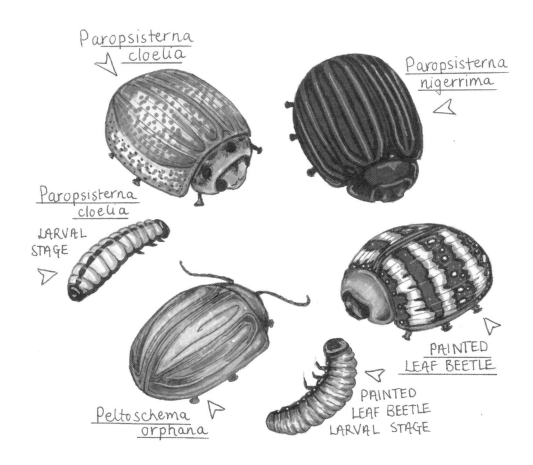

Paropsisterna cloelia

Paropsisterna nigerrima

Paropsisterna cloelia
LARVAL STAGE

PAINTED LEAF BEETLE

Peltoschema orphana

PAINTED LEAF BEETLE LARVAL STAGE

LEAF BEETLES

One warm November, I walked the loop through Dead Horse Gap up to the summit of Mount Kosciuszko, on Monaro-Ngarigo Country. On the return walk, I saw *thousands* of these shiny, round, golden-yellow beetles. They were happily munching on snow gums all over the slopes, creeping up tree branches, or clinging on to grasses. I even rescued a few from puddles where they were stuck, wearily waving their legs without purchase, held up by water tension. The trees everywhere showed signs of their munching and the further I walked, I saw just how extensively they were snacking through the canopies of the trees. Then I wondered maybe if I shouldn't have rescued those beetles out of the puddles, for the sake of the snow gums. I later discovered these were leaf beetles, the common name for beetles of the family Chrysomelidae. As you may have guessed, they love to eat a variety of native and introduced leaves.

This is a big and spectacularly varied group of insects, with over 2000 species of leaf beetles in Australia. They are busy little bugs, often clambering over foliage, up stems, and munching leaves with a hurried energy.

WHAT TO LOOK FOR A round, 10–12mm long beetle, often with beautifully patterned elytra. Some of these beetles can retract their antennae and heads partially under their shell, giving them another common name: 'tortoise beetle'. Their wide-set, dark eyes and colourful patterns make them look pretty dang cute, though several species are loathed for their pestilential-level snacking on eucalypt plantations. The larvae of leaf beetles are spiky grubs, which look like tiny caterpillars or spitfires (*see* p.73).

LIFE CYCLE Female adult leaf beetles generally lay eggs on food plants, often by chewing a divot out of the leaf surface and laying eggs in the groove. The eggs hatch into larvae, who feed on young leaves. When grown, they retreat from the tree down to burrow into the soil, where they pupate. They later emerge as adults, sometimes overwintering and resuming mating and egg-laying in the warm months of the next season.

WHERE TO LOOK Leaf beetles can be found all over the country, including Tasmania, though they are often relatively local, with certain species only found in specific areas. As both larvae and adult beetles, they rely on stands of healthy, foliage-rich native trees on which to feed. Head to local bushland reserves and scan the canopy or low hanging branches for activity. I also sometimes find leaf beetles near my parents' woodpile, where they have presumably dropped from the tree overhead, pupated, then emerged from the soil there.

WHEN TO LOOK Most leaf beetles are common in summer, but this will vary depending on the species.

SIMILAR SPECIES Pictured opposite are several species of native leaf beetles: eucalypt-feeding paropsine beetle (*Paropsisterna cloelia*), found in WA, SA, Victoria, NSW, southern Queensland and Tasmania; *Paropsisterna nigerrima*, found in WA, SA, Victoria, NSW and southern Queensland; painted leaf beetle (*Paropsis pictipennis*), found in south-east Australia; and *Peltoschema orphana*, found in Victoria and Tasmania. Christmas beetles (*see* p.85) and ladybirds (*see* p.101) look similar at first glance.

Cryptolaemus montrouzieri

◁ WAXY
SPIKY BODY
mimicking A
MEALYBUG

◁ MEALYBUG
DESTROYER
LARVAL STAGE

MEALYBUGS

◁

◁

MEALYBUG
DESTROYER
LADYBIRD
ADULT

◁

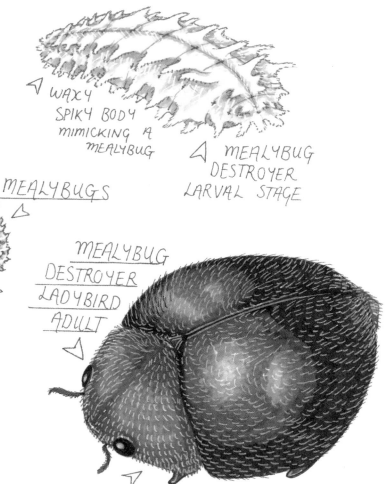

◁ FINE HAIRS
OVER BODY

MEALYBUG DESTROYER LADYBIRD

Mealybug destroyers are the big (on personality), bad, kind-of-adorable wolves of the insect world. Just when you thought ladybirds were delicate, meek beetles that roamed around your garden, observe the mealybug destroyer ladybird. This tiny beetle is only about half a centimetre long. However, much like a miniature 007 agent, these little critters use their size and wits to their advantage, readily infiltrating and feeding on mealybug infestations. Mealybugs are a sap-sucking insect, similar to aphids – a common frustration in gardens. Not the brightest, these pests are slow-moving, wingless, armour-less critters, making them easy prey.

It gets better though – the adult ladybirds, already happily snacking on mealybugs, also lay their eggs near mealybug infestations. When these eggs hatch, an impressive event occurs. Out from the egg crawls a larvae that looks impressively similar to a mealybug – waxy, spiky and white. Evolutionary pressures have led the mealybug destroyer to produce larvae that look just like mealybugs – a phenomena known as 'aggressive mimicry'. This larvae, a wolf in sheep's clothing, enters the mealybug infestation and, just like mum taught her, munches those unsuspecting pests. These tiny beetles are effective enough at controlling mealybugs that they have been introduced to multiple overseas locations, where they are used as a biocontrol to defend against pest bugs in food crops.

WHAT TO LOOK FOR A tiny, furry-looking beetle, about 5mm long. The head and thorax of the mealybug destroyer is an orange-brown colour, and the elytra are black. They have visible large, dark eyes, and their bodies are covered with a thin, felt-like covering. The larvae, as mentioned, are spiky little white grubs.

LIFE CYCLE An adult female mealybug destroyer will usually lay her eggs close to, or even amongst mealybug colonies. Mealybugs spread along the stem of plants in vegetable gardens, so a mealybug destroyer ladybird will generally hang near these colonies. The larvae emerge to predate the mealybugs, other scale insects, or even aphids for a couple of weeks, before they pupate, then emerge as adults.

WHERE TO LOOK Mealybug destroyer ladybirds are found most densely along the south and east coast of Australia, but are also sighted in south-western WA. Look in your garden, or at local orchards or community veggie patches.

WHEN TO LOOK Spring, summer and autumn.

HABITAT HELP Instead of using pesticides immediately on scale or aphid infestations in your garden, perhaps give it a couple of days and check regularly to see if some ladybirds have found the colony and started to feed on it. The ladybirds likely won't consume the whole colony of mealybugs, but can potentially make an impact on the numbers, protecting your plants from major damage. Looking after a vegetable garden without clearing native vegetation nearby will also be beneficial to many species of insects.

SIMILAR SPECIES Other ladybirds (*see* pp.98–101).

Illeis galbula

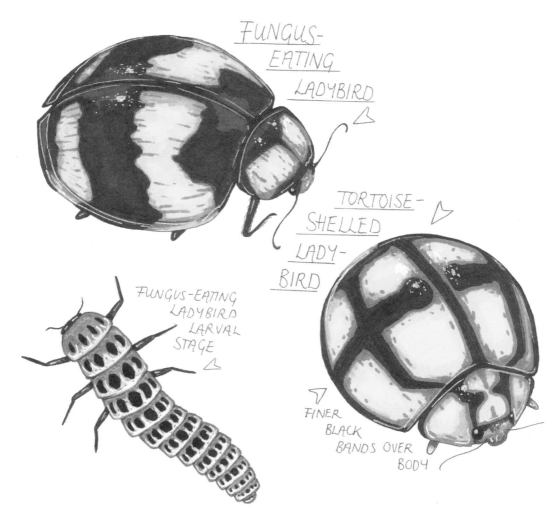

FUNGUS-
EATING
LADYBIRD

TORTOISE-
SHELLED
LADY-
BIRD

FUNGUS-EATING
LADYBIRD
LARVAL
STAGE

FINER
BLACK
BANDS OVER
BODY

FUNGUS-EATING LADYBIRD

Though not the most 'classic' ladybird in appearance, these tiny yellow and black beetles are discerning eaters, and a friend to gardeners in eastern Australia. While many other Australian ladybirds found in your garden feed on scale insects and other sap-sucking insects, these ladybirds feed on the fungus known as powdery mildew (*Odium* spp. fungi). This fungi often wreaks havoc across cucumbers, zucchinis and pumpkins. As most growers will have unfortunately discovered, the growth of white mildew on leaves usually signals the end of the squash season. However, the presence of these little fungi-eating (mycophagous) beetles may slow the tide of mildew in your veggie patch. Creeping across leaves and stems, these ladybirds feed on both the spores of the mildew, and on the hyphae (the root-like extensions of fungi) that the mildew expands along. Though their love of mildew sounds a bit peculiar, their dedication to fungus, I suppose, isn't too far off our human love of blue, stinky cheeses, or of a nice Swiss brown mushroom cooked in butter.

Fungus-eating ladybirds can survive over winter and therefore have to supplement their diet with pollen to survive when powdery mildew isn't in season.

WHAT TO LOOK FOR A small (about 5mm long), round beetle, with yellow-and-black patterning across the body. The outside of their body is slightly flattened, like a teeny version of the 'flange' on the outside of pie-dish beetles (*see* p.121). The larvae are spiky yellow-and-black grubs that roam around, also feeding on powdery mildew.

LIFE CYCLE After mating, adult females lay eggs on the underside of leaves. The larvae hatch and feed until they are ready to pupate. When ready, adults emerge to seek out some tasty fungus and a mate, often producing multiple generations in a good season.

WHERE TO LOOK The fungus-eating ladybird can be seen from Tasmania up to Cape York in northern Queensland. They are common in gardens, but you could also look for them in orchards, or local parks. The most likely way to see them is to look amongst mildew-affected plants in backyard gardens, usually in late summer when rains have allowed mildew to grab hold. I often see the adult beetles throughout spring and summer in the garden. Sometimes they fly and land on you, seemingly just to say 'hello' and check out the terrain of your arm for a bit.

WHEN TO LOOK As mentioned above, these ladybirds can survive over winter, especially where food is abundant, but are more commonly seen during spring and summer.

HABITAT HELP Avoiding or minimising use of pesticides in your garden is a great way to look after this species.

SIMILAR SPECIES The tortoise-shelled ladybird (*Harmonia testudinaria*, pictured opposite), is also found along the east coast; as is the common spotted ladybird (*see* p.101).

Harmonia conformis

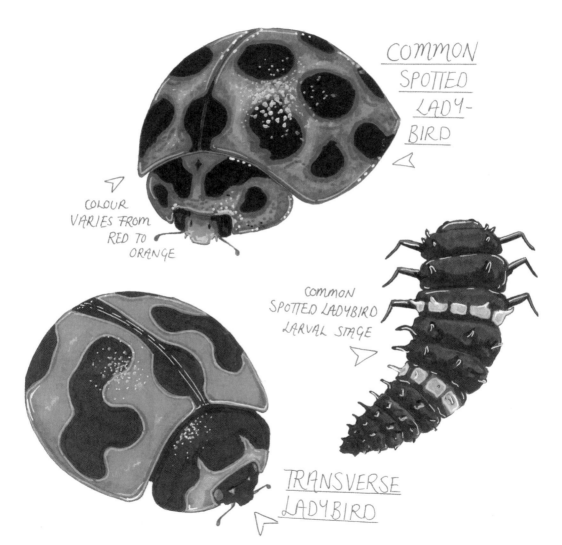

COMMON
SPOTTED
LADY-
BIRD

COLOUR
VARIES FROM
RED TO
ORANGE

COMMON
SPOTTED LADYBIRD
LARVAL STAGE

TRANSVERSE
LADYBIRD

COMMON SPOTTED LADYBIRD

Like a little orange gemstone, the common spotted ladybird is always a bright spark in the garden, whether they sit on a leaf, or whizz past your head to the next sunny perch. For those who have been lucky enough to have one pause for a rest on your finger or shirt, you'll be familiar with the sight of a ladybird 'powering up' for flight by lifting its hard elytra (wing covers), unfurling its soft membranous wings and whirring off. For such a seemingly delicate species, these tiny beetles are actually predaceous and, due to their dietary preferences, benefit somewhat from human vegetable gardens. As larvae and adults, they like to feed on garden pest species, such as scale insects and aphids. Backyard gardens, with various tasty cultivated species of plants, are places where aphid infestations readily emerge, so ideally (and often) that spells the presence of aphid-munching ladybirds and their larvae. That said, the adults, though also predatory, sometimes get their wires get a bit crossed, and just drink the honeydew from aphids – not so good for your beloved fruit trees. These tiny beetles will also feed on nectar to supplement their diet.

The adult ladybirds occasionally gather in huge parties on higher ground – known as 'hilltopping', like some butterfly species (*see* p.1) – where they gather for a big ol' swinging party with plenty of gene exchange.

WHAT TO LOOK FOR A yellow-orange beetle, about 5mm long, with black spots. However, there is a fair bit of colour variation in the common spotted ladybird, so you may see some that are a much deeper orange-red colour. Their larvae are a bit spidery-looking, with yellow-and-black markings.

LIFE CYCLE The adult females lay their eggs in a cluster on the underside of a leaf. The larvae hatch and usually seek out a nearby pest population of aphids or scale insects, and feed on them. When grown, the larvae will find a nook under a leaf, pupate, then emerge as an adult ladybird about a week later.

WHERE TO LOOK Common spotted ladybirds are found most densely along the east coast of Australia from Tasmania up into Queensland, in south-east SA, and in the south-west corner of WA. Suburban gardens, orchards and botanic gardens are great places to start looking for them.

WHEN TO LOOK Adults can be seen year-round, surviving over winter, but they seem to be most active and common in spring and summer.

HABITAT HELP Like the other ladybirds who dwell in human gardens (*see* p.97, 99), avoiding or minimising use of pesticides in your garden is a good way to look after this species.

SIMILAR SPECIES There are about 300 species of ladybirds in Australia, and many of them have similar body shapes and patterns, such as the transverse ladybird (*Coccinella transversalis*, pictured opposite), found across Australia.

Family
Buprestidae

ALYAWARR LANGUAGE
akarley-akarley (pronounced a-CAR-lee-a-CAR-lee), ('black jewel beetle', *Merimna atrata*).

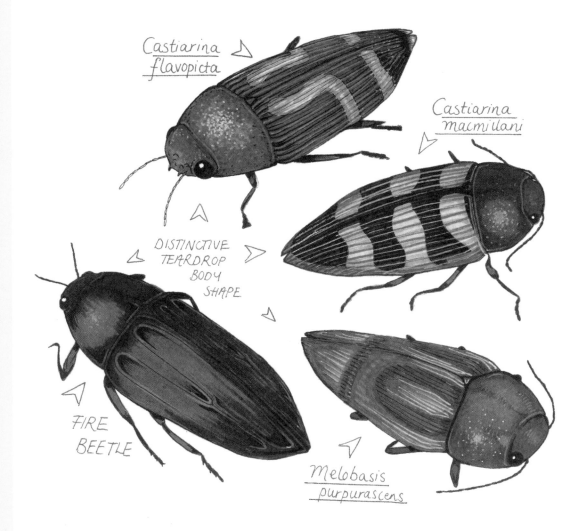

Castiarina flavopicta

Castiarina macmillani

DISTINCTIVE TEARDROP BODY SHAPE

FIRE BEETLE

Melobasis purpurascens

JEWEL BEETLES

Jewel beetles across the continent have largely the same body shape, but display an incredible array of colours and patterns. As a result, most of them do not have individual common names but are referred to by the umbrella term 'jewel beetles' or 'buprestids'. The beetles vary in their appearance to a spectacular degree, and most species have highly specific habits, relying on certain tree types for both feeding and reproduction. One species, known as fire beetles (*Merimna atrata*, pictured opposite), are drawn to areas where bushfires are burning. In these areas, on still-smouldering logs, they seek out a mate. Pretty hot, I know! Other jewel beetles primarily live and feed amongst flowering trees in bushland areas. Most jewel beetles are generally active during the day, especially in warm weather, when they trundle around in flowers, feeding on nectar, or sometimes feeding on leaves. Some species fly for impressively long distances between flowers, which likely assists in pollinating otherwise isolated plants.

On several bushwalks, I've been lucky enough to see jewel beetles crawling through banksia florets, or amongst shrubs on the sunny side of the track. However, I quickly learned that if you disturb a jewel beetle, they freeze and fall off whatever perch they're on, making a quick escape.

WHAT TO LOOK FOR Jewel beetles are an elongated oval shape, generally about 10mm long, though some can be as large as 60mm long, and some tiny species are only a few millimetres long. Many *Castiarina* species are dark with vivid patterning, such as *Castiarina macmillani* (pictured opposite, found in WA) and *Castiarina flavopicta* (pictured opposite, found in south-east Australia). Others, such as *Melobasis purpurascens*, found in south-east Australia, have a mother-of-pearl sheen to their bodies. Jewel beetle larvae are white grubs with flattened heads and wood-chewing mouthparts.

LIFE CYCLE Female jewel beetles lay eggs on a host plant. Some species' larvae have preferences for certain kinds of wood, while others are more general in their choice of host trees. After laying eggs, the hatched larvae burrow into and feed on the wood of the tree, where they grow, then pupate. After emerging as adult beetles they seek out a mate.

WHERE TO LOOK This insect family has over 1000 different species, so you'll have to use your location to try to narrow down which it could be. Jewel beetles can be seen all over the continent, including Tasmania. There are some species that specialise in more arid zones, while others have adapted to heathlands, or open woodland. The consistent factor is native forest, so keep an eye out when visiting areas of flowering bushland.

WHEN TO LOOK Due to the huge variety and distribution of jewel beetle species, some will have a year-round presence, while others will have brief adult seasons in only spring and summer when native flowers and new growth on trees is in abundance.

HABITAT HELP Australian jewel beetles are dependent on areas of established native vegetation with limited disturbance. You could create jewel-beetle friendly areas of your garden by growing patches of endemic plants. Another great way to support their habitat is to protect any remaining areas of native vegetation, be it in your backyard, bush reserves, or on nature strips where native plants remain. Every bit of habitat is helpful.

SIMILAR SPECIES Click beetles (*see* p.105) and net-winged beetles (Lycidae family).

Family Elateridae

WARLPIRI LANGUAGE
pirilyi-pirilyi (pronounced PIHR-ill-yee-
PIHR-ill-yee), ('click beetle').

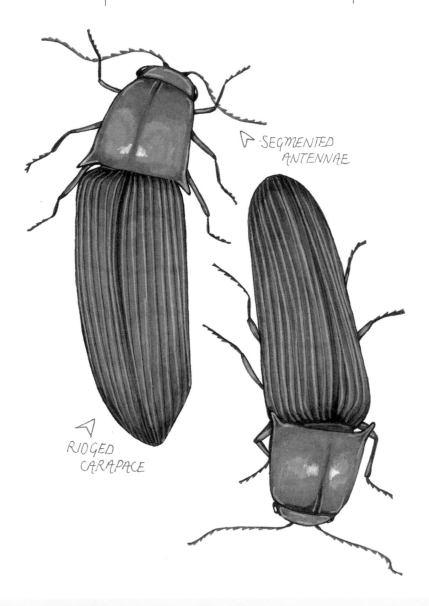

SEGMENTED
ANTENNAE

RIDGED
CARAPACE

CLICK BEETLES

Like me, as a kid you may have played with (or been scared by) click beetles, which are a common house visitor in the summer months. These unassuming, little beetles are well-represented in Australia with many different species going by the same common name. They often sit on the external walls of houses, drawn there by lights. Though most species are nocturnal, on one memorable spring hike, every signpost on the way to Mount Nelse on Jaitmatang Country in Victoria was *covered* with click beetles, as if they'd all decided to congregate for a party during the day.

Although they look superficially similar to jewel beetles (*see* p.103), click beetles use a different strategy for survival if disturbed. If hassled, they twitch and make an audible 'click' to both daunt would-be predators, and to flip themselves back onto their legs. This 'click' action is so powerful it tends to launch the beetles into the air to an impressive height (surely an advantage if you are being faced by a predator). The majority of adult click beetles feed on plant or organic matter, with some going in for a sip of nectar in flower florets when opportunity allows.

These beetles are found around the world, so I like to think that inspecting, picking up, and squealing in surprise at the 'click' of click beetles is a uniting feature of many people's childhood, no matter where you're from.

WHAT TO LOOK FOR Click beetles are generally about 20mm long, and usually brown or black in colour. The larvae are called 'wire worms', and have white segmented bodies with a slightly flattened head.

LIFE CYCLE Adult female click beetles lay their eggs in the soil, where the larvae hatch, feed on organic matter, pupate, then emerge as adults. The adults of some species can survive over winter, so are relatively long-lived, and you may encounter them sheltering amongst leaf litter or in your wood pile during the colder months.

WHERE TO LOOK Many similar-looking species of click beetles can be found all over Australia, including in Tasmania. *Conoderus tabidus* (pictured opposite) is a fairly typical species found in Victoria. You could walk around your house or garden at night with a torch, and inspect any insects perched on your walls or verandah. Otherwise, keep an eye out in local parks or botanic gardens, especially under bark, or amongst leaf litter during the day.

WHEN TO LOOK Spring and summer in the south, while some will survive through winter in the north.

SIMILAR SPECIES There are several hundred species of click beetles found in Australia and all have a relatively similar appearance. A beautiful specimen is *Ophidius histrio*, found in NSW and Queensland. Some jewel beetles (family Buprestidae, *see* p.103) have a similar body shape to click beetles, but are often much more brightly coloured.

Rhipicera femorata

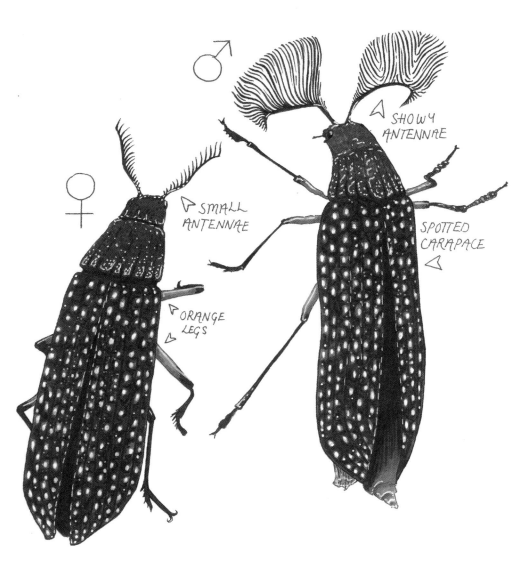

FEATHER-HORNED BEETLE

At Wilson's Promontory/Wamoon/Yiruk, I was walking along the beach when I noticed several blue-black beetles gripping on to grass tussocks in the breeze. Looking more closely, I could see these beetles had long, curling antennae, which shifted in the wind. Despite their enormous headgear, after periods of rest they readily flew about with their antennae tilting as if looking for a radio signal. Over the years, I've been lucky to see these beetles several times, and I'm always charmed by their mustachio-like antennae, which are only possessed by the male beetles. These large antennae are, in fact, sense organs used to detect female pheromones, and thus help the beetles to find a mate. So those fancy antennae are tiny biological radios, in a sense.

Despite their spectacular appearance, not a huge amount is known about these beetles, as there are only a few members of the genus, and their adult life is short-lived, making them hard to study, as is the case with many Australian insects. Members of this same group (genus *Rhipicera*) are also found in the northern hemisphere, where they are known to parasitise the larvae of cicadas, feeding underground before emerging. So the theory goes that Australian feather-horned beetles may do the same thing – hatch as grubs in the soil, seek out a cicada grub (such as the greengrocer cicada, *see* p.193), feed on it until ready to pupate, then emerge from the soil for their brief adulthood.

WHAT TO LOOK FOR A small beetle, about 20mm long, with large, curled antennae. These beetles are black (or almost a dark blue in the sunlight) with white spots on their wing covers. They also have orange-red legs. Females have smaller and less elaborate antennae than males.

LIFE CYCLE Though little is known of their life habits, it is likely that adult female feather-horned beetles lay eggs in the soil, where the grubs hatch, feed, pupate, and then emerge fully developed. The adults have a short reproductive lifespan, intent on seeking a mate for their brief period of time above ground, which will be your lucky chance to glimpse one.

WHERE TO LOOK These beetles are found in southern WA, SA and south-east Australia, with their range extending into southern Queensland. I've only ever seen these beetles in coastal heath, or amongst grasses on the beach itself, so looking in areas with sandy soils amongst coastal woodlands could be a good start.

WHEN TO LOOK Spring and summer.

SIMILAR SPECIES The other Australian species of feather-horned beetle, *Rhipicera reichei*, looks very similar to *Rhipicera femorata*, likely with the same life habits. Net-winged beetles (family Lycidae) also look superficially similar to feather-horned beetles.

Chauliognathus lugubris

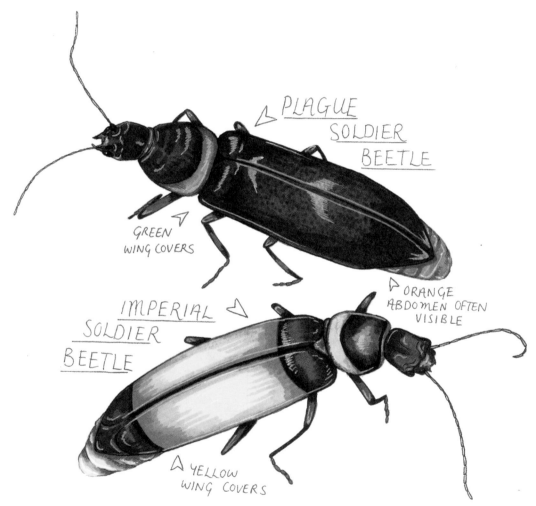

PLAGUE
SOLDIER
BEETLE

GREEN
WING COVERS

ORANGE
ABDOMEN OFTEN
VISIBLE

IMPERIAL
SOLDIER
BEETLE

YELLOW
WING COVERS

PLAGUE SOLDIER BEETLE

The plague soldier beetle is probably a familiar sight to you. These are common summertime visitors to gardens or bushland, and they readily defend themselves from disturbance by excreting a nasty-smelling fluid. Though at first glance these beetles are a little nondescript, they often make a memorable appearance in the warmer months of the year by gathering in *immense* clusters on trees, telephone poles, branches and bushes. Hence, their name – these beetle-parties give us a glimpse of what a true plague of insects may look like.

The soldier beetle larvae eat eggs and young stages of other insects, while adults are omnivorous, eating pollen, nectar and fellow invertebrates. Though they gather in large numbers on suburban plants, they don't seem to eat much foliage. Instead, this swarming tactic is primarily a way to gather together all the local adults for an opportunity to mate. Despite the harmless nature of these beetles, something about the sight of thousands of insects swarming over one another can be a little disconcerting. There is a fair bit of reassurance online for gardeners that, no, that *huge* crowd of beetles on your fruit tree aren't there to defoliate it – they're gathering to find mates, and drink nectar. Just a good ol' beetle orgy. I think of the plague soldier beetles as legions of Ancient Rome – insects that revel in wild Bacchanalian festivals for a short time in the warmer months, then quickly retreat to unseen fronts until the next season.

WHAT TO LOOK FOR A dark green beetle, about 15mm long, with an orange 'belt' across their middle, and a yellow abdomen (visible under the elytra/wing covers). The larvae tend to remain amongst soil and leaf-litter, so can be hard to spot.

LIFE CYCLE After eggs are lain by adult females, the grubs hatch to live in leaf litter and eat other small invertebrates. When well fed, they pupate, ready to emerge when the weather warms.

WHERE TO LOOK Plague soldier beetles can be seen from south-east Queensland around to south-east SA, and in Tasmania. Look in suburban gardens, your local park, botanic gardens, or in bushland. Usually where you find one beetle, you will find many others.

WHEN TO LOOK Late spring and summer.

SIMILAR SPECIES The imperial soldier beetle (*Chauliognathus imperialis,* pictured opposite), and the tricolor soldier beetle (*Chauliognathus tricolor*), both look quite similar. Many other species of soldier beetle – family Cantharidae – have a similar body shape and behaviours to the plague soldier beetle.

Phoracantha semipunctata

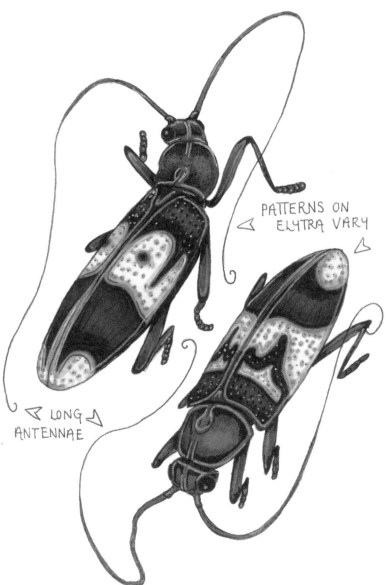

PATTERNS ON ELYTRA VARY

LONG ANTENNAE

EUCALYPTUS LONGICORN BORER BEETLE

Also known as 'longhorn beetles', the eucalyptus longicorn is a common beetle in eastern Australia, and has impressively long, curling antennae ('horns'). The adult beetles tend to feed on eucalypt foliage. However, as larvae these beetles present a slightly more intense challenge to native trees. These hungry grubs bore into wood, feeding and growing in tree tissues, out of reach of predators or parasites. Most species in this genus of wood borers (*Phoracantha*), primarily attack only damaged or stressed (often drought-stressed) native trees. Usually these beetles occur in low enough numbers that most trees survive a mild longicorn infestation. However, in recent times, perhaps due to dry conditions and high temperatures, the beetles have started to seriously diminish certain subspecies of snowgums in the High Country of Victoria and NSW. The warmer weather means longicorn beetles can access susceptible host trees in higher altitudes, dig deeper into the cambium of the tree, and complete generations more rapidly (growing faster in the hotter weather). As a result, these beetles often ringbark host trees, interrupting the flow of carbon and water through the plant, causing it to die. Similar breakouts of wood-boring longicorn beetles occurred in 2011 in the drought-stricken Northern Jarrah Forest of south-west WA. In some areas, you can spot the carved paths of the larvae in dead gum trunks, where their little gnashers have chewed through so much of the wood that the poor tree can no longer sustain itself.

Eucalyptus longicorn borer beetles are really quite beautiful to look at, but serve as a reminder of how readily a small environmental shift can toss ecological balance out of the window.

WHAT TO LOOK FOR A narrow, long-bodied beetle, about 25mm long. Their elytra (wing covers) are glossy brown and black, often bearing some zig-zag patterning. Males have longer, heftier antennae than females.

LIFE CYCLE Female longicorn beetles lay their eggs under the bark of a preferred host tree (*Eucalyptus* spp.). The eggs hatch and the larvae munch through wood, extracting nutrients until they grow big enough to pupate. After pupating, they clambour their way out as adults. Eucalyptus longicorn beetles can survive for several years in trees as larvae or pupae before emerging. Impressively, their long, patient lives in wood mean they have been inadvertently transported overseas, often developing inside eucalypt building planks that were then shipped to other countries. That means, reminiscent of the bentwing ghost moth (*see* p.31), several decades ago, some slightly dazed longicorn beetles emerged from eucalypt planks in Europe. Some of these exported insects have established pest level populations in overseas gum tree plantations, such as in California.

WHERE TO LOOK Although these beetles can be seen sparsely across the whole continent, eucalyptus longicorn borers are most densely concentrated in south-east SA, across Victoria, eastern NSW and eastern Queensland. Visit areas of eucalypt-dominant bushland during the warmer months.

WHEN TO LOOK Spring and summer.

SIMILAR SPECIES Australia has around 1300 recognised species of longicorn beetles – family Cerambycidae – and various kinds can be seen all over the continent. The genus *Phoracantha* are preferential gum-tree borers, and all have similar patterning and body shape.

Subfamily Luciolinae

PLAIN BEETLE
BY DAYLIGHT

WINGS
FOLD
BENEATH ELYTRA

LIGHT
ORGANS

LIGHT
ORGANS

FIREFLIES

On a dusk walk through coastal bushland, I found myself surrounded by winking lights. Starry little globes flashed from rocks on the ground, leaves on shrubs, and floated through the air between trees. By sheer luck, I had wandered through a group of adult fireflies, communicating by light signals. I'm surprised one didn't fly in to my open mouth, given how dumbfounded I was by the beauty of it. Fireflies, despite their name, are actually part of the beetle order, Coleoptera, and when seen in the daylight can easily be recognised as a member of the same order as feather-horned beetles (see p.107) and plague soldier beetles (see p.109).

By night, however, fireflies glide about, identified by the bright flashes they emit from the light organ in their abdomen. These flashes are a romantic advertisement between adult beetles, who survive for only a couple of days, unable to feed. For that short adulthood, they are driven by pure romance (or genetic desperation) to seek out a mate. The specialised light organ on the underside of their body takes in oxygen and combines it with a special compound called luciferin. Luciferin generates cold light, occurring in several bioluminescent organisms, including midshipman fish and ghost fungi. This compound emits the glow of light (and love) from the butts of these romancing beetles, allowing them to seek one another out during their brief adulthood. Amazingly, these beetles exert supreme control over their light emissions, creating complex flashing patterns that broadcast their suitability as a mate. How they dictate the chemical reactions within their bodies isn't yet understood, only adding to their mystique.

WHAT TO LOOK FOR Floating, flashing little lights at night! The adults are about 10–12mm long, with dark wing covers. Under the elytra, the pale light organ at the tip of the abdomen can be seen. The larvae are about 10mm long, with layered, segmented bodies.

LIFE CYCLE Light displays occur at night so mates can seek one another out (females often perch and wait for males to come to them). Adult pairs mate and, in the same season, the females lay their eggs. The larvae hatch, and cruise around until the following spring, feeding on snails in damp woodlands. In late spring or early summer, the larvae pupate and emerge for their brief mating flight as adults – and the cycle begins anew.

WHERE TO LOOK Fireflies can be seen along the eastern coast of Queensland and NSW. Warm, humid bushland areas are the most likely locations, with some ephemeral sightings have been made in more southern regions of NSW. Head into bushland at dusk, or your local park or nature reserve.

WHEN TO LOOK Adult fireflies are usually active for only a few weeks of a year. They can be seen year-round, but are more common in warm conditions, especially in more southern areas of their range.

HABITAT HELP Conserving areas of rainforest and bushland can protect Australian fireflies.

SIMILAR SPECIES There are 25 species of firefly that can be seen in Australia, but encountering them is a matter of being at the right place at the right time, making a sighting quite exceptional. By day, adult fireflies look a bit like plague soldier beetles (see p.109).

Family Staphylinidae

Creophilus
erythrocephalus

DIFFERENT
SPECIES MAY
VARY IN COLOUR

ELONGATED
SEGMENTED
ABDOMEN

Thyreocephalus spp.

ROVE BEETLES

Rove beetles are part of the family Staphylinidae, and pictured opposite are two of the more distinct Australian species (*Creophilus erythrocephalus, Thyreocephalus* spp.). There are many others in this family in Australia, all of them colloquially known as rove or whiplash beetles. This family of beetles is commonly seen crawling through soil or amongst grasses in suburban backyards. They tend to have flattened, long bodies, a rounded head, small elytra (wing covers) containing (sometimes non-functional) wings, and a long tail – which, in combination, can make them look just a little disconcerting. To add to the effect, they can arch their elongated abdomen up over their head almost like a scorpion, and some produce a yucky smell to scare off predators. This combo deal – long body, reared tail and nasty smell – all combine to give this beetle a sinister reputation, one that's carried through several different cultures across the globe. In Ireland, some rove beetles are known as a *deargadaol* (meaning 'devil's beast'). It's also sometimes known as the coffin-cutter beetle, the devil's footman, or, my personal favourite: the devil's coach horse.

These beetles feed on other insects, especially maggots and carrion feeders, and some soft-bodied invertebrates like earthworms. As a result, they are common in soils where organic matter is breaking down, drawn there by the allure of potentially snackable critters. Some are more generalist feeders, consuming fungi and detritus. Despite their fierce reputation, when I've encountered these beetles, they usually just scurry away to try to hide in the garden.

WHAT TO LOOK FOR A long-ish beetle (often measuring about 20mm, though there is a lot of size variation in this family), usually scurrying quickly over the ground or through grass. Some appear brown, green or red, but most species are black.

LIFE CYCLE Rove beetles usually mate, then lay eggs in leaf debris near carcasses or rotting wood (in short, places where the emerging larvae will be able to find other insects to consume). The larvae are active and mobile, seeking out prey. After the larvae feed, grow and pupate, the adults emerge to renew the cycle.

WHERE TO LOOK The various species of this family can be seen all over Australia, including in Tasmania. They are less common in arid regions.

WHEN TO LOOK Year-round, though they are more active during the warmer months.

SIMILAR SPECIES Pictured opposite are just two examples of the many species of rove beetles that can be seen in Australia, and pretty much all of them have a very similar body plan. You might also mistake some earwigs (*see* p.131) for a rove beetle – though rove beetles do not have cerci (pincers) at the tip of their abdomen. Some tiny thrips look a bit like rove beetles, but tend to fly away and have a forked tail.

Family Passalidae

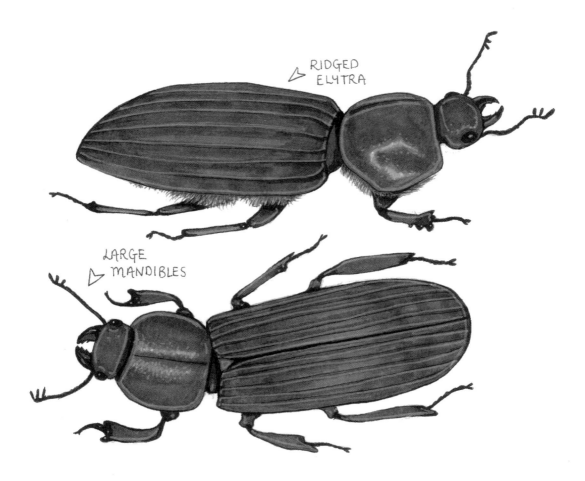

RIDGED ELYTRA

LARGE MANDIBLES

BESS BEETLES

Also known as passalid or patent leather beetles, bess beetles are shiny black insects that often emerge from the soil if you're digging around in your garden. They are lovers of rotting wood, and thus are an important part of the ecosystem, as they help to decompose organic matter into new soil, allowing nutrients to be recycled. They have rather fierce-looking mandibles, but these are just to assist with their wood-chomping ventures.

While many beetles are largely solitary, bess beetles sometimes live in small family groups, burrowing a network of shared tunnels in fallen logs. They communicate with one another by rubbing their hardened elytra (wing covers) against part of their abdomen (known as stridulation, a bit like what grasshoppers and katydids do). Most beetle parents mate, lay eggs and turn tail without a backward glance, but bess beetles stick around to ensure the welfare of their kids. They chew the rotting wood into a purée, constructing a bundle of wood-mash and beetle-poop to house their eggs. It's theorised that this bank of wood-pulp and poop means the soft-jawed larvae can both feed immediately after hatching, and by doing so, inoculate themselves with the helpful microbes that their parents have in their gut. Just like kimchi, sauerkraut or kombucha is good for your microbiome, bess beetle poop, it seems, is full of important microbes for their young grubs.

WHAT TO LOOK FOR Large-ish black, shiny beetles, about 20–25mm long, with big mandibles. Their elytra (wing covers) have long grooves, like mini corrugated-tin sheets. The larvae are white grubs with dark heads, of a similar length to the adult beetles.

LIFE CYCLE Eggs are lain, usually in a little 'bank' of parent poop and mushed-up wood. The eggs hatch and larvae emerge, feed, grow and eventually pupate inside the family gallery. They then emerge as fully-fledged adults.

WHERE TO LOOK Bess beetles can be seen along the east coast, from Cape York in far-north Queensland to south-east SA, and in Tasmania. Look (carefully) around rotting wood, in your backyard if you have a firewood pile, or amongst tree-fall or debris (look up first to make sure no weak branches are overhead). I've also encountered these beetles whilst digging soil in the garden, where they've roamed from their wooden homes.

WHEN TO LOOK Year-round, though they are most active during the warmer months of the year.

HABITAT HELP As occupiers of decomposing wood, bess beetles benefit from having logs and large branches that have a big enough diameter to house their small commune of beetles. We often think of the aspects of the forest that are upright – standing trees and shrubs – but the layer of decomposing organic matter, including fallen trees, are a very important habitat for many invertebrates. Leaving dead wood may seem counter-intuitive in a space-restricted garden, but it can provide amazing resources to some really cool insects.

SIMILAR SPECIES There are about 30 described species of bess beetle in Australia, all quite similar in appearance and habit. At first glance, you may confuse a bess beetle with some darkling beetles (*see* p.123) or rove beetles (*see* p.115).

Calosoma (subgenus *Australodrepa*) *schayeri*

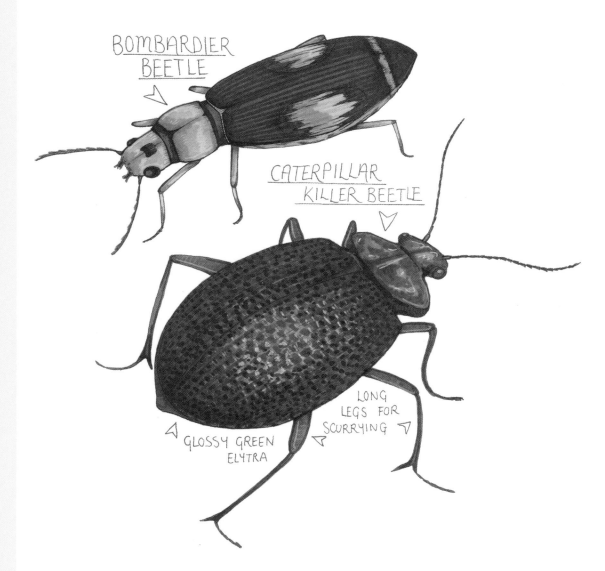

BOMBARDIER BEETLE

CATERPILLAR KILLER BEETLE

GLOSSY GREEN ELYTRA

LONG LEGS FOR SCURRYING

CATERPILLAR KILLER BEETLE

Imagine life as a bird: you're hungry after a long afternoon of soaring over the bushland of the Great Dividing Range. Your sharp avian eyes discern a glittering, metallic green beetle clambering over the soil. It looks juicy and delicious, so you move in to strike, but just as you get close, this little beetle oozes a nasty-smelling liquid from its rear end, and while you try to shake the smell out of your beak, the beetle scrambles off into the leaf-litter, never to be seen again. Like the clever fireflies (*see* p.113) and the Baphomet moth (*see* p.49), the caterpillar killer beetle proves that insects really are wonderful chemists. While caterpillar killers are an entrancing emerald colour, their predatory behaviours are a little less tasteful, hence their killer name. They love to feed on soft caterpillars, which they munch while they roam amongst leaf litter, bark and decomposing wood. If disturbed, they release a nasty smelling acrid liquid, a defensive mechanism found in many of the ground beetles (family Carabidae), of which the caterpillar killer is a member.

Although all that sounds pretty dark – eating squishy, helpless caterpillars and all – carabids, including caterpillar killers, are beneficial to farmers and gardeners, as they can partially diminish populations of larvae when they become excessive, rather like parasitic wasps (*see* p.63). Ideally, the presence of both caterpillars and caterpillar killers will be in a good balance for a time when populations are booming.

WHAT TO LOOK FOR Adult beetles are about 15mm long, metallic green, with a rounded abdomen and long legs. They also have fierce mandibles for slicing-and-dicing caterpillars (wince). The larvae of the caterpillar killer beetles look almost like black centipedes, with segmented, narrow bodies.

LIFE CYCLE Adult female caterpillar killer beetles lay their eggs in decaying wood or rich soil. The eggs hatch and the larvae emerge to roam around in the leaf litter, where they feed on smaller insects until they are ready to pupate. When ready, an adult caterpillar killer beetle emerges.

WHERE TO LOOK Caterpillar killers can be seen sparsely across Australia, excluding the northernmost regions of WA, the NT and Queensland. The adults habituate leaf litter or decaying wood where they feed on the larval stages of insects, so look in bushland, parks or in healthy gardens.

WHEN TO LOOK These beetles can be seen year-round, though they are much less active and less commonly seen in the cooler months.

SIMILAR SPECIES There are about 2500 described species of ground beetles in Australia, and they are a very diverse group. The bombardier beetle (*Pheropsophus verticalis*, pictured opposite), sprays hot, acidic liquid from its rear as a defense mechanism. It has two chemicals in its abdomen that, when mixed, become volatile and corrosive – kind of like a molotov cocktail. The bombardier beetle is seen sparsely around Australia's coastal regions, excluding Tasmania.

Subtribe Heleina

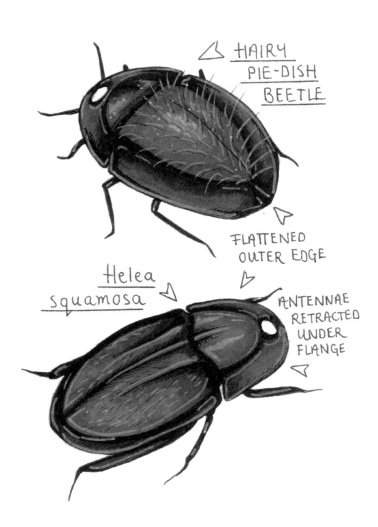

△ HAIRY
PIE-DISH
BEETLE

FLATTENED
OUTER EDGE ◁

Helea ◁
squamosa

ANTENNAE
RETRACTED
UNDER
FLANGE ◁

PIE-DISH BEETLES

In my opinion, pie-dish beetles are the endurance pilgrims of the Australian outback, a little bit like a Robyn Davidson of the insect world. Making tracks through some of the most harsh and remote areas of the country, pie-dish beetles are efficient, self-reliant beetles, their little dish-shaped bodies rocking gently as they move over the ground. These peculiar beetles can be found across most of the continent, but are particularly tough, and readily survive in dry, hot areas of the country where food and water are only intermittently available. *Helea squamosa* (pictured opposite), survives in the Simpson Desert and its surrounds, while the hairy pie-dish beetle (*Helea perforata*, pictured opposite) survives in south-west WA. Many other pie-dish beetles in the subtribe Heleina can be seen across Australia, adapted to a variety of different ecosystems.

These little beetles are often nocturnal, scurrying about in the dark, feeding on fungi, plant matter, seeds, and occasionally scavenging dead insects. During the day, they will generally find cover in leaf litter, under bark or in burrows, waiting for the cover of darkness. In extremely arid areas like the Simpson Desert, they enthusiastically burrow themselves under the sand to avoid the hot sun. Already a very diverse group, pie-dish beetles are actually part of the larger family of darkling beetles (*see* p.123).

WHAT TO LOOK FOR Pie-dish beetles are round-bodied, dark and leathery looking, usually about 15mm long. True to their name, they have flattened bodies with a slightly upturned outer edge (known as a 'flange'). As a part of the darkling beetle family (Tenebrionidae), they can vary greatly in appearance and ability (for example, some in the genus *Pterohelaeus* can fly, while other pie-dish beetles cannot). The larvae of pie-dish beetles are pale yellow, segmented grubs.

LIFE CYCLE Adults generally lay eggs in a burrow or nook somewhere safe – ideally close to food sources for their soon-to-be-hatched larvae. The larvae, when hatched, live in the soil, feeding and growing, until ready to pupate, then adults emerge from the soil.

WHERE TO LOOK Pie-dish beetles can be seen across the continent, from rainforests in Queensland to dry areas of SA and WA, proof of their toughness and adaptability. As they are particularly successful in arid areas, you could head to open, dry regions to look for them. Some species are active during the day, but in hotter, drier areas, you're likely to have more luck at night when it's cooler.

WHEN TO LOOK Year-round, but less commonly seen over the winter months.

SIMILAR SPECIES There are many species of pie-dish beetles in Australia, all with the peculiar upturned 'rim' to their body. If you see one, try snapping a photo, and compare your image with others on citizen science apps (*see* p.xxv) to see if you can ID it. Other species in the darkling beetle family (Tenebrionidae, *see* p.123) are ground-dwelling beetles that have similar behaviours.

Amarygmus spp.

SHINY IRIDESCENT CARAPACE

FAINTLY DOTTED ELYTRA

DARKLING BEETLES

The innocuous, diverse and prolific darkling beetles are always a delightful sighting. The name 'darkling beetle' was established by the naturalist Linneaus in the 1700s, describing these insects as 'seekers of dark places'. The origin for the darkling beetle family name, Tenebrionidae, is from the Latin *tenebrio*, a term used for 'one who loves darkness'.

Despite the slightly spooky overtones of this name, darkling beetles really are just shy critters that want to stay out of sight. They are soil or forest-litter dwelling creatures that feed on decaying plants and other detritus, living on plant and fungal matter, with the occasional invertebrate thrown in the mix. Like bess beetles (*see* p.117), they are essential recyclers in ecosystems, so we should appreciate their diligent munching efforts. In Australia alone, there are about 1600 known species of darkling beetle (so far), and all of these beetles are diverse, including the pie-dish beetle group (*see* p.121). I've chosen to feature only one darkling beetle genus (*Amarygmus*) for this entry, however many other types of darkling beetles can be seen across all of Australia.

WHAT TO LOOK FOR The *Amarygmus* darkling beetles are usually shiny, have a rounded, ridged abdomen, and a squat head with segmented antennae. They range from 8–15mm long. Larvae look almost like millipedes, with yellowish segmented bodies and dark heads. Also known as mealworms, darkling beetle larvae are common poultry feed.

LIFE CYCLE Adult *Amarygmus* darkling beetles can live from months to years, sometimes overwintering, whilst other species will die as adults at the onset of winter, leaving their eggs to produce the next generation of beetles. After the eggs hatch, the larvae live in the soil, eating and growing until their pupal stage, then emerge as adults.

WHERE TO LOOK *Amarygmus* darkling beetles can be seen along the east coast, from Victoria to Cape York in far-north Queensland. They are more densely seen in wetter forested areas. Look for them in your local bush reserve or parkland, and peek (carefully) under rocks, between logs and amongst leaf litter. While *Amarygmus* darkling beetles are concentrated on the east coast, other darkling beetle species can be found across all of Australia, from coastal regions, through to drier and less vegetated areas.

WHEN TO LOOK Year-round, though less commonly seen over winter.

SIMILAR SPECIES *Amarygmus* darkling beetles – of which there are about 50 species – all look alike and occupy similar habitats. As mentioned, pie-dish beetles are part of the darkling beetle family so they can look similar, as can bess beetles, and some ground beetles (*see* p.119).

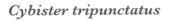

Cybister tripunctatus

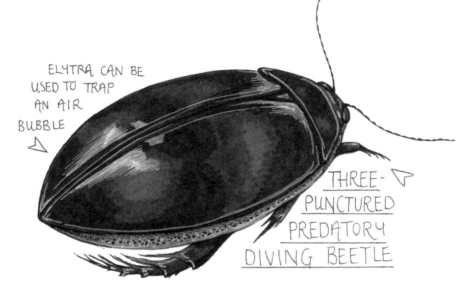

ELYTRA CAN BE
USED TO TRAP
AN AIR
BUBBLE
▷

THREE- ▽
PUNCTURED
PREDATORY
DIVING BEETLE

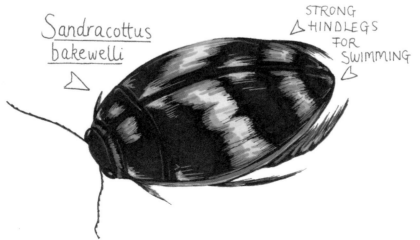

Sandracottus
bakewelli
▷

STRONG
△ HINDLEGS
FOR
SWIMMING
△

THREE-PUNCTURED PREDATORY DIVING BEETLE

These fierce insects live in freshwater bodies, feeding mostly on insects, but also taking on tadpoles and sometimes even managing to capture small fish. Not only the adult diving beetles are hunters – even their larval stage, known as 'water tigers', have large, scary-looking mandibles that they use to feed. Both of these life stages breathe through the tip of their abdomen, retreating back to the surface after a dive to refill their oxygen stores. To assist with longer hunting stints underwater, adult diving beetles can trap an air bubble under their elytra (wing covers), which forms a little air-pocket over their abdomen, allowing them to use it like a weird entomological scuba tank. These astounding beetles are basically underwater astronauts, gliding through the water effortlessly as they pursue prey.

If this level of adaptation wasn't enough for you, adult diving beetles can even fly. They can swim *and* fly. What more do you want? They take flight to move between water sources, especially during seasons when ponds dry up or become diminished of food quickly. They seem to use the reflected light on water sources to navigate to new habitats, but are sometimes confusedly drawn to glassy surfaces that reflect light in a similar way to water.

WHAT TO LOOK FOR The three-punctured predatory diving beetle is about 25mm long, with a shiny, oval-shaped body, and long, bristly back legs to assist in swimming underwater. The larvae (water tigers) are long, segmented critters, usually hanging tail-first at the surface of the water when not hunting.

LIFE CYCLE Adult diving beetles usually lay eggs on or in the stems of plants near to a slow-moving freshwater source. The eggs hatch and the water tigers generally hang just under the surface of the water, with the tip of their abdomen arched upwards to touch the water surface. If food is spotted, they can swim down and hurriedly grab it. Having fed and grown, diving beetle larvae pupate somewhere on the bank nearby, then return to the water as adults.

WHERE TO LOOK The three-punctured predatory diving beetle can be seen across Australia. Look in still or slow-moving water bodies, such as in lazy creeks, dams, puddles,

drainage ditches or ponds, especially where there is plenty of other insect and frog life.

WHEN TO LOOK Year-round, depending on water availability and seasonal conditions.

HABITAT HELP The best way to support predatory diving beetles is to protect existing areas of freshwater habitat. This involves maintaining native aquatic plant populations, limiting erosion, and avoiding the pollution of waterways (e.g. minimising runoff, avoiding pesticide use near water).

SIMILAR SPECIES There are over 200 species of predatory diving beetles known in Australia (family Dytiscidae), many with similar habits and body shape to the three-punctured predatory diving beetle, including the beautiful *Sandracottus bakewelli* (pictured opposite). Whirligig beetles (*see* p.127), burrowing water beetles (Noteridae), and crawling water beetles (Haliplidae) could also be mistaken for predatory diving beetles.

Family Gyrinidae

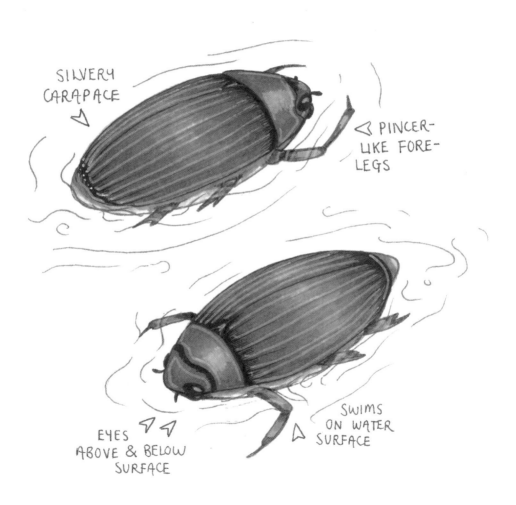

SILVERY CARAPACE

PINCER-LIKE FORE-LEGS

EYES ABOVE & BELOW SURFACE

SWIMS ON WATER SURFACE

WHIRLIGIG BEETLES

When I first saw a whirligig beetle up close, I thought: these little creatures are definitely the lobsters of the insect world. These freshwater-dwelling insects are well adapted for their environs, with streamlined bodies that easily 'skate' around on the surface of the water. Whirligig beetles are such strong swimmers that they can navigate fast-flowing streams as well as standing ponds without too much trouble. Sometimes you see a whole bunch of them hanging out on the surface of waters, swooping around in circles – they move so quickly that they can look like ball bearings bouncing on the water surface.

Most strikingly, whirligig beetles have two pincer-like forelegs that they use for grabbing little snacks (ahem, insects). Though they can dive, the beetles tend to swim across the surface instead, where they can readily grab and consume any small invertebrates that land in the water. They even have an extra pair of eyes to help them hunt (though, these are technically considered a single pair of eyes, 'split' into the above-water and below-water aspects.) They have the expected set on their head, which sit above the waterline, and the second set is almost like a mirror image, sitting *underneath* the surface of the water, allowing them to see above and below the water at the same time. If all this adaptive genius wasn't enough, the Johnston's organ, located in their antennae, makes the beetles sensitive to the teeny waves of an insect struggling on the surface of the water.

WHAT TO LOOK FOR A small, silvery-looking beetle, about 10mm long, scooting around on the surface of a freshwater source. If you get a closer look at these beetles you'll see their lobster-like forelegs. (The other two pairs of legs are reduced and stubby, assisting with swimming, while the forelegs are all about meal-grabbing).

LIFE CYCLE Female adult whirligig beetles lay eggs amongst submerged vegetation. Like mosquitoes (*see* p.163) and dragonflies (*see* p.139), the larval stage of whirligig beetles is aquatic, feeding on small invertebrates in the water. Having fed and grown, the larval stage eventually emerges from the water to pupate. When ready, the pupa hatches and an adult whirligig beetle emerges to live a surface-skating life.

WHERE TO LOOK There are about 20 species of known Australian whirligig beetles and they can be seen all over the continent, including in Tasmania. The best bet is to head to a local pond, lake, dam, stream or drainage channel to see if you can spot them. As they rely on other insect life for food, try to find more established water bodies (rather than ephemeral puddles). Most species of whirligig beetles are very small, so it's best to sit near a still water body for a while with your attention on the surface of the water, looking for rippling movements. Sometimes sitting at an angle where the light shines off the water can be helpful.

WHEN TO LOOK Spring through to autumn, though populations of whirligig beetles vary greatly depending on the seasonal conditions and water availability.

SIMILAR SPECIES Predaceous diving beetles (*see* p.125) and water striders (*see* p.187).

Amitermes meridionalis

ALYAWARR LANGUAGE
ampeng (pronounced am-POONG-a), ('winged termite' or 'flying ant').

GUMBAYNGGIRR LANGUAGE
julumbaling (JOO-loom-bah-ling), ('termite mound').

WARLPIRI LANGUAGE
jakumirnta (JAHK-oo-meern-ta); *pama-pardu* (BAH-ma-BAR-doo); *panjirti* (BAHN-jir-dee); *yartuyunyu* (YAR-too-YOON-yoo), (terms for termite species).

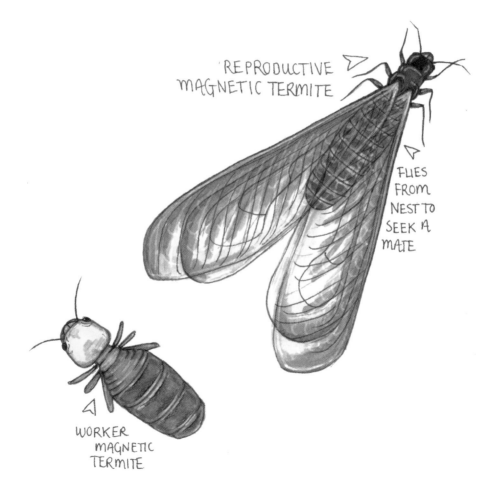

'REPRODUCTIVE MAGNETIC TERMITE

FLIES FROM NEST TO SEEK A MATE

WORKER MAGNETIC TERMITE

MAGNETIC TERMITE

All round, termites get a bad rap, but in reality they are truly strange and amazing creatures that are very effective at enduring in harsh environments. Instead of dealing with the outside world, they create hard structures in which they live out their entire life cycle, excluding a few lucky individuals who get to take nuptial flights outside to seek a mate. They feed on various forms of plant tissue – usually grasses, true wood, or decayed organic matter in soils, playing an important role in decomposition and nutrient recycling. Like ants (*see* p.67) and some wasps (*see* p.61), termites are 'eusocial', meaning they have complex social structures, allowing them to cooperatively achieve more than any solo insect could.

Of the termites, magnetic termites are particularly unique strategists. If you've ever been in northern Australia and seen a greyish, tombstone-like mound of earth jutting up above the savannah, then you're likely to have seen a magnetic termite mound. True to their name, these structures are always magnetically aligned. The slender axis of the colony runs north–south to maximise the early morning and late afternoon sun, and avoid the intense heat of the midday sun. By doing so, they keep the internal atmosphere of the mound at a bearable temperature, protecting both the brood and adult workers inside. I find it amazing that these tiny little critters can obey climactic cues to such an accurate degree.

WHAT TO LOOK FOR Tombstone shaped mounds, square-ish, grey, about 1–2m high (although colonies can be as high as 4m). Though the typical magnetic termite mound is relatively smooth, some have slightly more folded or tubular shapes, but they always point north–south. You are more likely to spot the mounds rather than adult termites out and about.

LIFE CYCLE A magnetic termite colony lives to sustain itself, and each population typically houses an egg-laying queen, who once a year (often towards the end of the wet season) raises fertile males and females. This new generation of termites then exit the nest on a 'nuptial flight' to start new colonies. Ideally, fertile termites from other nearby colonies will be out looking for love too, adding a few more genes to the mix. After mating, a queen starts a new colony from the ground up, raising her own workers who form a mound from clay, sand and termite saliva. Workers tend the young, defend the colony, and head out at night to gather food.

WHERE TO LOOK Seen from Larrakia to Yolngu Country, in the northernmost areas of the NT, they are generally seen out in flat, open and undisturbed areas of grassland.

WHEN TO LOOK Year-round. Termite mounds, like diamonds, are forever. Well, almost. Termite mounds can be very long-lived, as a queen (who herself may live to produce eggs for many years) will be replaced if she dies. If you were to visit some magnetic termite mounds right at the start of the rainy season, there's a chance you'll see the fertile male and female reproductive termites leaving the colony to seek a mate.

HABITAT HELP Helping to preserve native grasslands and floodplains is an important way to support not only magnetic termites, but also general invertebrate biodiversity.

SIMILAR SPECIES Other species of termites can be seen in Australia, all with various forms of earthen mounds, subterranean colonies or in-tree colonies. On some warm nights great drifts of winged termites may appear in your area.

Titanolabis colossea

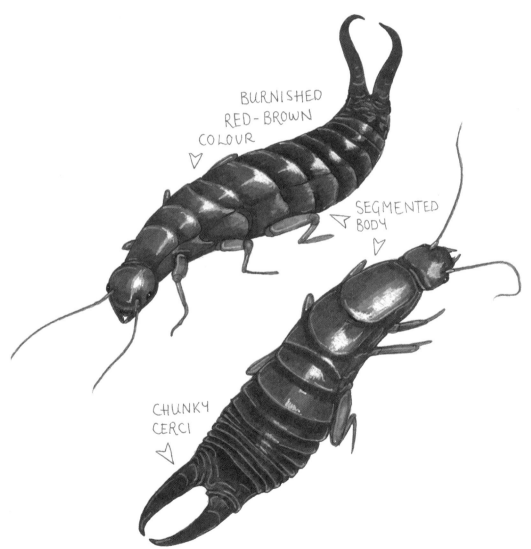

BURNISHED
RED-BROWN
COLOUR
∨

SEGMENTED
BODY
∨

CHUNKY
CERCI
∨

GIANT EARWIG

I realise that earwigs are usually thought of as the things that scare you by scurrying out of the veggies you bought at the farmers' market but, honestly, there are a lot of things to appreciate about these humble insects. Because they feed on detritus, they assist with nutrient recycling. Unlike most insects, earwig mums remain beside their nesting burrows to care for their growing kids. And, despite the scary looking pincers and the creepy name, they don't crawl into your ears while you're sleeping. Those long pincers on the tip of their abdomen (called 'cerci') are used for a number of other things – sometimes to defend against threats, sometimes to hold prey, and sometimes to hold on to one another during reproduction.

In eastern Australia, we have a glorious native species known as the giant earwig, who is nearly 5cm long. These rarely-seen earwigs live in rotting wood in bushland, trundling over landscapes to seek food and a mate. Unfortunately, there is very little known about their life habits, despite being the largest known living earwig in the world. Native Australian earwigs, as generalist snackers, eat some small invertebrates, rotting vegetative matter and other detritus, but also have a predilection for pollen, so they sometimes hang out in flowers (kinda cute). Just remember, earwigs are actually just shy little animals, even if they look a bit scary.

WHAT TO LOOK FOR A huge (5cm long), lush, rusty brown and black earwig, with wide cerci at the tip of its abdomen, and a fairly broad body (they're kind of the pickup trucks of the insect world.)

LIFE CYCLE Interestingly, female earwigs actually parent their eggs and young nymph earwigs. Being a solo mama, she digs a short burrow in soil or decaying wood, lays her eggs, and remains nearby to defend them. She even cleans the eggs to prevent any fungal or parasitic infections. After hatching, she may even help to feed the young nymphs, as they slowly grow in size, moult and develop into their largest adult form. Usually you can distinguish the younger nymphs by their smaller size.

WHERE TO LOOK In eastern Victoria and NSW, these insects like to hide out in nooks and crannies, amongst decaying wood, leaf litter, or under bark. Though they're rarely spotted, if you're walking in the forests of eastern Australia perhaps you'll get lucky and see one scurrying through leaf litter.

WHEN TO LOOK Year-round, but these insects are most active during the warmer months.

SIMILAR SPECIES The most common earwig species people encounter tends to be the introduced European earwig (*see* p.202), who often turns up in houses at inopportune moments. However, Australia has many species of native earwig, so it's worthwhile trying to distinguish between them.

Ellipsidion australe

WARLPIRI LANGUAGE
minyinjirri (pronounced MIN-yin-jir-dee),
('cockroach', 'spinifex beetle').

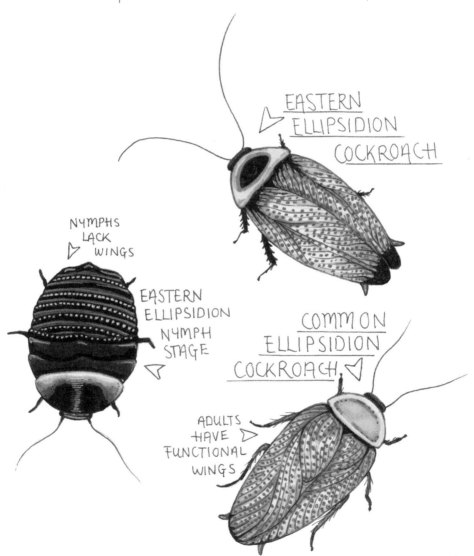

EASTERN ELLIPSIDION COCKROACH

NYMPHS LACK WINGS

EASTERN ELLIPSIDION NYMPH STAGE

COMMON ELLIPSIDION COCKROACH

ADULTS HAVE FUNCTIONAL WINGS

EASTERN ELLIPSIDION COCKROACH

Wait, wait, wait, before you skip this page, I have something important to tell you. Like you, growing up, I quickly developed a learned fear of cockroaches. They were always fast-scurrying, yucky bugs that indicated dirtiness or disease. However, having read more about Australian native cockroaches, I've come full circle, because ultimately they don't really do anything more gross than other insects. Besides, look at them. *Look.* How handsome are these roaches? These beautiful, harmless insects are a regular springtime and summer visitor to our garden, and are quite distinct from the household cockroaches you may encounter more regularly (often the most common household cockroaches are introduced species).

Though the eastern ellipsidion is a similar body shape to introduced cockroaches, their habits are different. They love to sunbake on perches, they feed on flowers and pollen, and when they're in an exploratory mood, I've often found them hiding out amongst the grapevine, or on the railings of the verandah. With their long antennae and delicate golden wing covers, these cockroaches really are worth a closer look – even their nymph stages are beautifully patterned and delicate looking. If I fell into a Kafkaesque nightmare and woke up as a giant cockroach, I wouldn't mind if it happened to be the eastern ellipsidion cockroach. Sunbake and eat flowers all day long? Sounds okay to me.

WHAT TO LOOK FOR A golden-coloured cockroach, about 15mm long, with delicate, veined wings, and a dark (almost black) spot over its thorax. They also have very long, fine antennae. The nymph stages are possibly even prettier to look at than the adults – they are a shiny brown-black, with each body segment traced by lines and dots of pale yellow. The young ones also tend to be quite round too, though they elongate as they mature.

LIFE CYCLE After mating, a female eastern ellipsidion will produce an ootheca (an egg case, *see* p.xix). She deposits this egg case in a safe place, where the eggs will hopefully remain undisturbed. Nymphs hatch from the ootheca, disperse, then feed and grow into adulthood.

WHERE TO LOOK The eastern ellipsidion cockroach is most commonly seen along the eastern coast of Australia, but can also be sighted much more sparesely in coastal regions of SA, WA and the NT. Keep an eye out for them in bushland reserves, heathlands, botanic gardens and parklands.

WHEN TO LOOK Spring and summer.

HABITAT HELP As feeders on flowers and pollen, one of the best ways you can support native cockroaches is to plant plenty of native flowering shrubs in your garden, if you have the space. One other great way to contribute to species' protection is to help other people to admire them for their beauty and diversity.

SIMILAR SPECIES There are several other 'ellipsidion' cockroach species that look quite similar, such as the common ellipsidion cockroach (*Ellipsidion humerale*, pictured opposite), which has a similar range.

Laxta granicollis

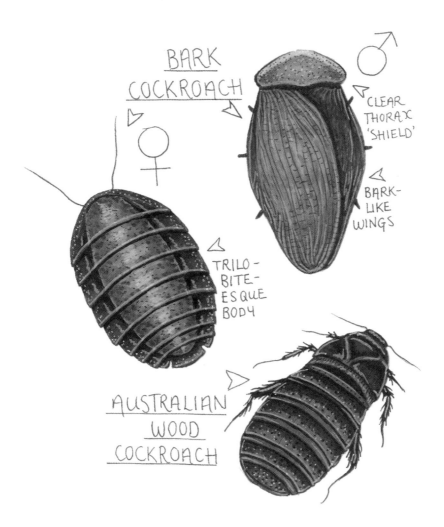

BARK
COCKROACH

♂

CLEAR
THORAX
'SHIELD'

BARK-
LIKE
WINGS

♀

TRILO-
BITE-
ESQUE
BODY

AUSTRALIAN
WOOD
COCKROACH

BARK COCKROACH

These oft-dismissed, harmless native cockroaches are a regular sighting near my house, usually congregating towards streetlights or moving around backyards on spring and summer evenings. Also known as a 'flat cockroach' or sometimes the 'trilobite cockroach', the bark cockroach is a common insect that likes to munch organic matter in your garden, and therefore acts as a nutrient recycler in the ecosystem. These cockroaches are sexually dimorphic (the male cockroaches look different to the females), with the males having dark, glossy wings, and females having no wings, but a segmented body. Despite their varied appearance, they are both beautifully camouflaged in native bushland against tree bark or amongst leaf litter.

I've often seen these cockroaches in the Dandenong Ranges, drawn to the kitchen window by the light. They are pretty wary, and often if caught (carefully) in a glass, will play dead to try to be left alone, lying on their back with their legs curled up. If you leave them undisturbed a while though, they usually get themselves flipped over again to scurry about. During the day, they hang out under tree bark, and sometimes shelter amongst rocks or in leaf litter – they'd much prefer to be outside in your garden than in your house.

WHAT TO LOOK FOR A dark, oval cockroach with a shiny body and long fine antennae, about 25mm long. Males are more of a classic cockroach shape, with two dark overlain wings, and a transparent shield over their thorax and head. They are very glossy and, despite whatever supposed 'creep factor' cockroaches have, are quite beautiful when you take a proper look at them. The females are a beautiful freckled brown, and look a little like a trilobite or crustacean. Nymphs look much like adult females.

LIFE CYCLE After mating, the female bark cockroach will produce an ootheca (an egg case, *see* p.xix). She keeps this ootheca internally, unlike some other cockroach species who deposit the egg case in a safe place. The eggs develop and hatch from the unharmed mother, to disperse, feed, and grow into adult bark cockroaches.

WHERE TO LOOK Bark cockroaches can be seen in south-east SA, across Victoria, eastern NSW and south-east Queensland. They are nocturnally active, so grab a torch and look outside your house or near streetlamps or fluorescent lights at campgrounds. Otherwise, you may have luck looking during the day amongst leaf litter or in secluded spots under tree bark. Local bush reserves and parklands are good places to try.

WHEN TO LOOK Year-round.

SIMILAR SPECIES Other *Laxta* species can look quite similar to the bark cockroach, as does the Australian wood cockroach (*Panesthia cribrata*, pictured opposite), another native species that is often encountered in backyards.

Polyzosteria mitchelli

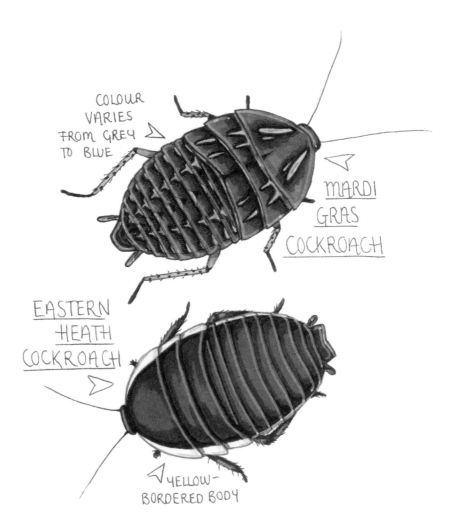

COLOUR VARIES FROM GREY TO BLUE ▷

MARDI GRAS COCKROACH

EASTERN HEATH COCKROACH ▷

◁ YELLOW-BORDERED BODY

MARDI GRAS COCKROACH

I very clearly remember my first encounter with one of Australia's striking *Polyzosteria* cockroaches. I was hiking along a trail in the Blue Mountains on Dharug and Gundungurra Country in NSW. On the trail ahead of me, I saw a striking yellow-and-black cockroach, sunning itself in the middle of the path. It was enormous (about 6cm long), and when I approached it to get a picture, it lifted up its little toosh and waggled it at me, as if telling me to back off. I retreated to watch it a little longer and I was struck by just how much of an *animal* this cockroach was: big enough to demand space, and also spectacularly beautiful. Although many of the genus *Polyzosteria* are mesmerising, I want to feature one particularly glorious specimen here: the mardi gras cockroach. This colourful critter is a mellow insect that likes to roam around in the wild, grazing on pollen, leaves and flowers – and has no intention of entering your house or scaring you by crawling across the ceiling while you're having a shower.

Interestingly, most cockroaches are thought of as humid-loving creatures, but the mardi gras cockroach thrives in drier areas. There is something endearing about these solitary cockroaches, like landships moving across the hot soils of Australia. The 'toughness' that imbibes most household cockroaches with an alarming degree of un-killability, endears the desert-dwelling mardi gras cockroach with an admirable sense of endurance and sturdiness. These insects are also known as Mitchell's diurnal cockroach.

WHAT TO LOOK FOR A large (up to about 50mm long) cockroach with copper-brown, greenish-blue and yellow patterns. They have a body segmented like a trilobite or slater, and mardi gras have blue legs.

LIFE CYCLE Adult cockroaches come together briefly to mate. The female then produces an ootheca (egg case, *see* p.xix), which contains the fertilised eggs. She will carry the ootheca around until she finds a good spot to dig it into the soil and leave it. The eggs eventually hatch, and the nymphs emerge to feed, grow and moult, until they develop into their spectacular adult form.

WHERE TO LOOK These critters can be seen from south-west WA, across the Nullarbor Plain to western Victoria, where they lumber around in scrublands, salt marshes, sand and heath, like a slow-moving work of art.

WHEN TO LOOK In the warmest months of the year.

SIMILAR SPECIES The genus *Polyzosteria* has several other species, another being the alpine metallic cockroach cockroach (*Polyzosteria viridissima*), a classic sighting in Victoria and NSW High Country, or the aforementioned eastern heath cockroach (*Polyzosteria limbata*, also known as the Botany Bay cockroach, pictured opposite), found in eastern NSW.

Hemicordulia australiae

GUMBAYNGGIRR LANGUAGE
garrarrana (GAH-rrah-rrah-nah),
('dragonfly').

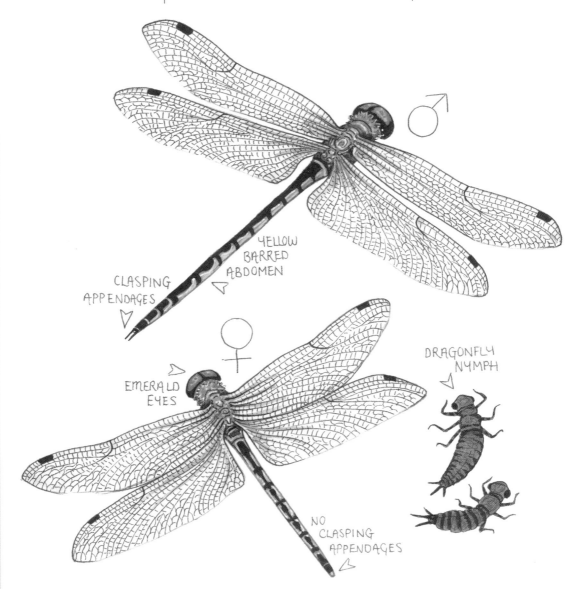

♂

YELLOW
BARRED
ABDOMEN

CLASPING
APPENDAGES

♀

EMERALD
EYES

DRAGONFLY
NYMPH

NO
CLASPING
APPENDAGES

AUSTRALIAN EMERALD DRAGONFLY

Dragonflies are seemingly so delicate and fast, it's hard to imagine that their life prior to adulthood is lived entirely underwater. Adult dragonflies lay eggs in or close to freshwater sources, where their nymphs will be able to hatch and begin hunting prey of smaller invertebrates. These predatory baby dragonflies live under the surface until they are ready to emerge from the water and moult into adult dragonflies. The Australian emerald is one of the more common species of dragonfly in south-east Australia, and in south-west WA. I often see emerald dragonflies at the local lake, where they buzz overhead by mere centimetres when I'm swimming, often intermingling with other species of dragonfly. If you watch closely, you'll sometimes see an emerald making a trip to shore with a small bundle of prey held firmly in its tiny legs, like the metal claw in an arcade game.

Also known as sentry dragonflies, these predatory insects are commonly seen skimming low over bodies of water, or scouting along the edges of streams where smaller insect prey hide (who are probably shivering in terror.) I think emerald dragonflies have a robot-like energy about them, as they seem unable to create a curve in flight, instead moving in sharp corners and zig-zags. There's something ruthless about the way they just scour the banks, make their selection, grab and go, unsympathetic to the little moth that was probably just having a nap on a leaf. I almost never see emerald dragonflies perch, instead they seem to be perpetually on the hunt for food or for a mate, which can make identifying them difficult.

WHAT TO LOOK FOR A green-eyed dragonfly with yellow markings, about 50mm long. At the tip of the abdomen in male dragonflies, there are two little pincer-ish looking bits (known as 'claspers', used during mating). Nymphs are stout-bodied aquatic critters.

LIFE CYCLE An adult female dragonfly oviposits (lays) eggs in mud or vegetation close to a freshwater source. Upon hatching, the nymphs enter the water, where they feed on smaller invertebrates and go through several moults (*see* p.xiii). They emerge from the water to undergo their final moult into adult dragonflies, ready to buzz about, hunting and seeking a mate.

WHERE TO LOOK Australian Emerald dragonflies can be found in WA, SA, NSW, Victoria, Queensland and Tasmania. They hunt other insects, including midges and small moths. They tend to hunt close to or over water, especially in sunny weather (though this may equally be a matter of the dragonflies being easier to see in the sunlight). Your best bet is to head to a local freshwater source (lake, pond, dam or creek), and sit for a while, watching the surface of the water.

WHEN TO LOOK Australian emeralds are most commonly seen in spring and summer.

SIMILAR SPECIES There are several similar-looking species of 'emerald' dragonflies that can readily be spotted, such as the Tau emerald (*Hemicordulia tau*), common in south-west SA and south-east Australia, including Tasmania.

Multiple species in the genus *Petalura*

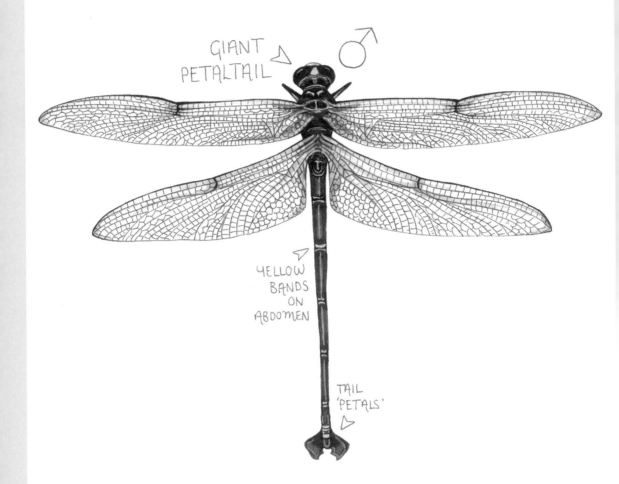

GIANT PETALTAIL ♂

YELLOW BANDS ON ABDOMEN

TAIL 'PETALS'

PETALTAIL DRAGONFLY

When I was studying geology, my lecturer described a period of late Paleozoic history when giant dragonflies – known as predatory griffinflies – roamed the jungles of Earth. These predators had a wingspan of around 70cm and, to me, this knowledge was equal parts awesome and terrifying. One part of my brain immediately considered whether I could toss some reins onto a giant dragonfly and hitch a ride. The *other* part of my brain said 'death by giant dragonfly mandibles would suck'. Anyways, when you see one of Australia's giant petaltail dragonflies, you'll know what I mean. While not a metre long (closer to 12cm), they are still pretty dang huge, with a wingspan larger than their body length – sometimes 16cm across.

Once, in the Budawang range in Yuin Country in NSW, a south-eastern petaltail dragonfly (the slightly smaller cousin of the giant petaltail dragonfly pictured opposite), zoomed right over my shoulder and perched on a stump ahead of me. It was big. Too big. For proof that I did indeed see an insect that large, I took an extremely blurry photograph that looked like FBI surveillance footage, but at least I preserved a sense of scale. These dragonflies are so large that their flight is audible – a thumping sound like a minute helicopter. In the humid, daze-inducing heat of the Corang Arch trail in the Budawangs, I half expected 'Fortunate Son' to echo from the petaltail as it flew past me to descend to its landing pad.

WHAT TO LOOK FOR A large brown-and-yellow dragonfly, around 120mm long in the case of the Queensland giant petaltail, *Petalura ingentessima*. Other petaltails tend to be a bit smaller, though all eastern petaltails have yellow bands on their abdomens. The western petaltail has a dark abdomen and pale brown thorax. Only the male dragonflies have the two little flaps at the end of their abdomen, hence the name 'petaltail'. These appendages are a great way to identify these dragonflies.

LIFE CYCLE Female petaltail dragonflies lay their eggs in the mud around water sources, especially in marshland or bogs. Upon hatching, the nymphs burrow into the mud, and from there they predate smaller invertebrates. As they feed, they go through several moults, until they finally crawl to the surface, undergo a final moult, and emerge as fully-grown petaltails.

WHERE TO LOOK Along Australia's east coast, and in south-west WA. Your best bet is to head to boggy or marshy areas of bushland, or look in coastal bushland near freshwater sources.

WHEN TO LOOK Your best chance of seeing a petaltail dragonfly is in late spring and summer.

SIMILAR SPECIES All petaltails are quite similar, excepting some size variation and distribution. The giant petaltail (*Petalura ingentessima*, pictured opposite) is found on the Queensland coast; the south-eastern petaltail (*Petalura gigantea*) is found on the NSW coast; the coastal petailtail (*Petalura litorea*) lives along the northern NSW and southern Queensland coasts; and the western petaltail (*Petalura hesperia)* is found in south-west WA.

Rhyothemis graphiptera

ALYAWARR LANGUAGE
rwewapimperr (pronounced ROW-a-pimp-erd-a), ('dragonfly').

WARLPIRI LANGUAGE
jirriri (JI-rear-ree); *jitiri* (JIT-ear-ree); *ngirnti-wirarra* ((i)-NGEARN-dee-WEIR-ah-dah), (terms for 'dragonfly').

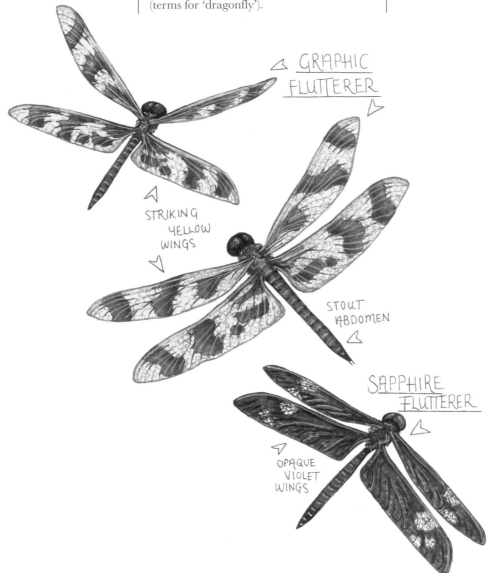

GRAPHIC FLUTTERER

STRIKING YELLOW WINGS

STOUT ABDOMEN

SAPPHIRE FLUTTERER

OPAQUE VIOLET WINGS

GRAPHIC FLUTTERER DRAGONFLY

The graphic flutterer is simply so striking, you're guaranteed to remember it once you've seen it. Whereas the giant petaltail dragonflies (*see* p.141) have size on their side, and the Australian emerald dragonfly (*see* p.139) wins in terms of population, graphic flutterers have artful patterning to set them apart. These dragonflies have four yellow-tinted wings, as if they were made of stained glass. In fact, all the members of this genus, *Rhyothemis*, have gloriously patterned wings, ranging from blues to black-and-gold.

The graphic flutterers, earning their name, have a distinctive pattern of wingflaps. When sailing over reeds and ponds, they move with a fluttering, rapid flight. When they perch on stems or branches near water, they seem to move their wings independently of one another (unlike most other dragonflies I've seen, which seem to keep their wings in 'unified' movement). These are small dragonflies with stout abdomens, but are fairly visible with their striking wings. Like other dragonflies, graphic flutterers hunt smaller invertebrates, usually by cruising around the edges of water bodies where insect life is thick.

WHAT TO LOOK FOR A small (about 30mm long) dragonfly, with a dark body, and large yellow wings, about 70mm across.

LIFE CYCLE An adult female graphic flutterer lays eggs in soft soil or plant stems near water. When these eggs hatch, nymph dragonflies emerge and creep into the water, where they feed and grow. Eventually they emerge from the water, moult one last time, and harden into their adult form, ready to roam, hunt and mate.

WHERE TO LOOK Graphic flutterer dragonflies can be seen in northern WA, along the coast of the NT, and along the east coast of Queensland and NSW. These dragonflies hunt for smaller invertebrates, so looking along freshwater sources – rivers, lakes, ponds – and in nearby bushland, where the dragonflies land and rest, are great places to start.

WHEN TO LOOK You're most likely to see a graphic flutterer dragonfly in spring or summer.

HABITAT HELP Protecting freshwater areas and marshlands is an excellent way to support dragonfly species. This includes creating ponds or rockpools in your garden (these should be well aerated with a small solar pump or flowing water to prevent mosquitoes from habituating).

SIMILAR SPECIES All five species of *Rhyothemis* dragonflies in Australia have patterned, beautiful wings, such as the sapphire flutterer (*Ryothemis princeps,* pictured opposite) found on the northern Queensland coast; and the yellow-striped flutterer (*Ryothemis phyllis*), seen along the coastlines of the NT, Queensland and northern NSW.

Ischnura heterosticta

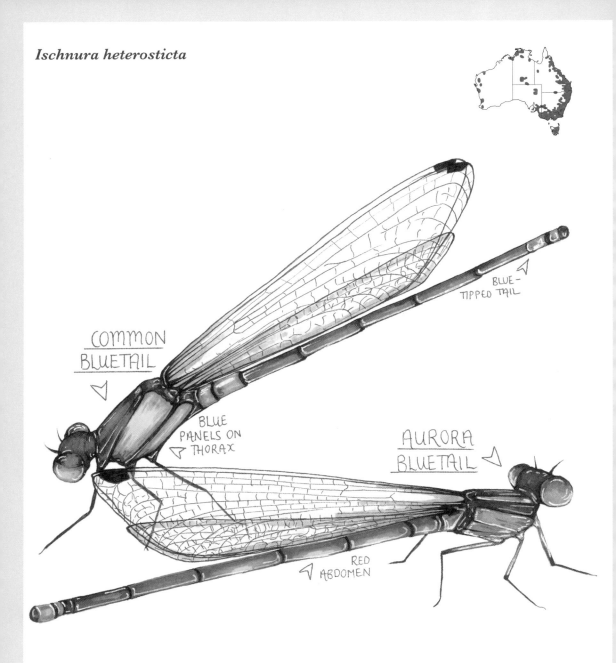

COMMON
BLUETAIL

BLUE-
TIPPED TAIL

BLUE
PANELS ON
THORAX

AURORA
BLUETAIL

RED
ABDOMEN

COMMON BLUETAIL DAMSELFLY

Like me, you may have seen a damselfly many times but haven't distinguished it as a different type of insect from a dragonfly. Damselflies, though very closely related to dragonflies, are part of the suborder Zygoptera (dragonflies are part of the suborder Epiprocta). They are often much smaller and more delicate than dragonflies and when at perch, damselflies rest their wings back along their thorax and abdomen, rather than at 90-degrees like a dragonfly (*see* p.139). Additionally, damselflies have smaller eyes that are more widely spaced on their head than dragonflies.

This particular species, the common bluetail, is one of the more widely seen species of Australian damselflies, so you should have a good chance of seeing one in the warmer months. With their vivid blue colouring, these small insects are easily seen with a bit of patience near most freshwater sources. I often spot common bluetails along the marshy creek banks amongst banksia forest, where they perch on reeds between short flights. Like dragonflies, damselflies predate smaller flying insects.

WHAT TO LOOK FOR A slender-bodied insect, about 35mm long, with two pairs of transparent wings. The head, abdomen and tail-tip are blue. Female common bluetail damselflies have a bit of colour variation, so may appear more green or brown than the bright blue of the males. The larval stage of damselflies are small and look much like dragonfly nymphs. They have three 'gills' which look almost like feathers emerging from the tip of their abdomen.

LIFE CYCLE Eggs are lain on debris in fresh water, such as floating leaves or wood, usually in a nook where water is slow moving or stagnant. Nymphs emerge from the eggs and start their underwater life, predating smaller invertebrates. After feeding and growing, the nymphs crawl from the water, moult a final time, and become adult damselflies.

WHERE TO LOOK The common bluetail can be seen all over Australia, including Tasmania. Looking near freshwater sources, like creeks, dams, ponds, well-watered parks or golf courses, is your best bet. Even better, if you head to areas where there is less human disturbance, such as in a national park, or along a lake edge, you might get a good glimpse of one.

WHEN TO LOOK The common bluetail damselfly can be seen from spring through to early autumn, though adults may be present year-round in more northern climes.

SIMILAR SPECIES Many of the Australian damselflies look very similar to the common blue tail, including the aurora ringtail, the swamp bluet (*Coenagrion lyelli*) and the wandering ringtail (*Austrolestes leda*). All three species from the genus *Ischnura* look very similar, such as the Aurora bluetail (*Ischnura aurora*, pictured opposite), found across Australia.

Suhpalacsa subtrahens

CLUBBED
ANTENNAE

LARGE
MANDIBLES

TAIL
RAISED
AT PERCH
IN 'TWIG'
POSTURE.

LARVAL
STAGE

YELLOW
STRIPE
DOWN
ABDOMEN

COMMON OWLFLY

At first glance, an owlfly gives the impression that a butterfly was perfectly crossed with a dragonfly. These predatory insects have large eyes, clubbed antennae and a cylindrical abdomen, much like a butterfly, but have the transparent and beautifully veined wings of a dragonfly. Interestingly, owlflies fold their wings downward when they land, lifting their abdomen out at an angle from their perch. Some researchers suggest this is an effort to look like a snapped-off twig or stem and, with their muted colouring, this can be quite an effective means of camouflage. Unlike oft-flying dragonflies, the common owlfly tends to be conservative with its energies, perching much of the time, and taking short bursts of flight when pursuing smaller flying insects to feed on. They also tend to hunt during the twilight or dawn hours (termed 'crepuscular', rather than nocturnal or diurnal).

While the adults are delicate and conservative hunters, the larvae of owlflies actually possess *huge* forcep-like jaws (mandibles). The hungry larvae use their jaws to grab and hold their prey, proving just as fierce as their adult counterparts. They look very much like antlion larvae (*see* p.149), although they do not dig pit traps to capture their prey.

WHAT TO LOOK FOR A brown, dragonfly-like insect, about 50mm long, usually perched (or occasionally flying) in open native forest or near watercourses. They have long, clubbed antennae, a yellow stripe down the length of their body, and transparent, downward-folding wings. The larvae are small, brown, round-bodied insects with large, serrated mandibles.

LIFE CYCLE An adult female owlfly will lay her eggs on plants or grass stems. The eggs hatch and the larvae spend their youth in soil or leaf debris where they hunt smaller invertebrates. Unlike dragonflies, who moult through several stages into an adult form, the owl fly larvae pupate in the leaf litter, later emerging as adult owlflies.

WHERE TO LOOK The common owlfly can be seen in eastern Australia from northern Queensland to Melbourne/Naarm. These insects require plenty of other insect life to hunt, and vegetation to hide amongst, so look in gardens, parkland, and bushland. Investigate little 'broken twig' shapes – they may be an owlfly in disguise.

WHEN TO LOOK Spring and summer are the most likely seasons to see adult owlflies.

SIMILAR SPECIES Lacewings (*see* p.153), dragonflies (*see* p.139), damselflies (*see* p.145). All owlflies (family Ascalaphidae) look relatively similar, such as the yellow owlfly (*Suhpalasca flavipes*) which has a similar range to the common owlfly.

Myrmeleon acer

ALYAWARR LANGUAGE
kwatyel ntyeny-ntyeny (pronounced
KWAITCH-il (i)n-JIN-yin-jin-ya); *mwet-mwet*
(MOOT-a-moot), (terms for antlion larvae).

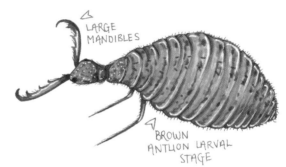

LARGE
MANDIBLES

BROWN
ANTLION LARVAL
STAGE

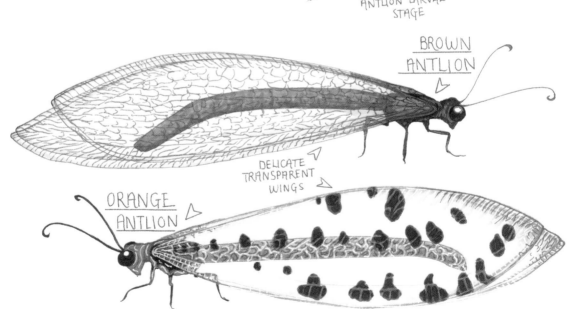

BROWN
ANTLION

DELICATE
TRANSPARENT
WINGS

ORANGE
ANTLION

BROWN ANTLION

BROWN ANTLION

The adult antlion, however delicate-looking, is actually preceded by a much fiercer and wily larval stage. Like the owlfly (*see* p.147), antlion larvae have *huge* pincer-like mandibles that they use to grab prey. However, it's not a simple matter of pursuing insects and grabbing them. Instead, like a miniature sandworm of the *Dune* franchise, the antlion constructs a steep-sided pit-trap in sandy soils. Digging downward in a spiral, kicking out sand as it goes, the antlion creates a hole. This pit is so steep-sided that any unwitting critter that wanders into it has a tough time getting back out again. Trap constructed, the antlion remains disguised beneath a layer of sand in the bottom of the pit, waiting for the tell-tale tremors of an insect desperately trying to scurry back up-slope. The antlion larvae emerges lightning-fast, and grabs the victim in their huge mandibles. Their most common – or perhaps preferred – victim is usually an ant of some variety, hence the name 'antlion'. The antlion essentially sucks out the body fluids of the victim, tossing the empty shell of the insect out of its pit-trap like a spent juice box.

The oft-overlooked adult form is fairly well-camouflaged in appearance and is short-lived. They are pretty clumsy, misguided fliers, as if they don't quite know how to manage their large dragonfly-esque wings as they seek out a mate.

WHAT TO LOOK FOR A brown insect with transparent wings, about 40mm long. The common brown antlion looks both like a damselfly, and also a bit like an owlfly, albeit with short, bent-tipped antennae. The larvae are brown with small heads and, frankly, terrifyingly huge mandibles.

LIFE CYCLE Adult female antlions lay eggs in soil or leaf litter. The eggs hatch, and the emergent larvae trundle off to build sand traps and to feed and grow. When ready, they build a cocoon in the soil where they pupate. Eventually an adult antlion crawls from the cocoon to the surface, allows its wings to expand and dry, then flies off (clumsily) to look for a mate, its savage youth forgotten.

WHERE TO LOOK The common brown antlion is most often seen in eastern Australia, but is also sparsely present in southern WA, the NT and south-east SA. Look in suburban gardens, botanic gardens and bushland reserves. Adult antlions tend to be most active around dusk.

WHEN TO LOOK Look for adult antlions during spring and summer, though they may experience longer seasons in Australia's north.

SIMILAR SPECIES Orange antlions (*Callistoleon erythrocephalus*, pictured opposite), seen along the Queensland and NSW coastlines; lacewings (*see* p.153), dragonflies (*see* p.139) and damselflies (*see* p.145).

149

Multiple species in the genus *Atalophlebia*

MAYFLY

One morning in Bright, Victoria, I woke up to find a mayfly perched on the camp table, so tired it couldn't move. It had probably drifted up from the Ovens River to land, exhausted and nearing the end of its short existence. As I got a closer look, I was particularly struck by this tiny critter's delicate body, which somehow survives these knocks and buffets of weather and environment to reproduce. I ended up taking it over to a nearby shrub so it didn't spend its last hour of existence sitting on a formica camp table, wondering where it went wrong in life.

These insects, whose adult form survives only a matter of hours, have long been a muse of poets, artists, and poorly considered YOLO tattoos. Mention of the mayfly even occurs in one of the oldest texts of all time: *The Epic of Gilgamesh*. These species are part of the order Ephemeroptera which, from the word 'ephemeral', refers to the very short life of the adults who live just long enough to mate, lay eggs, then die. Ironically, mayfly larvae can be quite long-lived, sometimes spending over a year in the water, feeding on debris, growing and shedding, before emerging as time-poor adults. Sometimes I wonder if, a la Christopher Nolan's *Inception*, the deeper dream – or the tinier you get – the slower the passage of time. So maybe a day feels like a lifetime for a teeny mayfly? I hope so.

WHAT TO LOOK FOR A tiny, brown, dragonfly-esque critter, with two pairs of wings (though the rearward pair are tiny and difficult to see.) The nymphs look almost like little anaemic underwater crickets, and have three 'prongs' extending from the tip of their abdomen.

LIFE CYCLE Like mosquitoes (*see* p.163), adult male mayflies swarm, often above water sources, in a big cloud, into which females enter and seek a mate. A mated female then lays her eggs on the water surface and, often enough, completely spent (or happily having fulfilled her destiny?), she floats on the surface of the water until picked off, usually by fish. The eggs drift down to stick to submerged rocks or other debris, hatching into larvae. After feeding and growing, the nymphs emerge from the water where, on the banks, they moult one further time to reach adulthood.

WHERE TO LOOK Mayflies in the genus *Atalophlebia* can be seen most densely in Australia's south-east, including Tasmania. These insects need relatively clean water in which to develop,

so their presence can be a handy bioindicator of good water quality. Walk along the banks of a dam, pond, creek or stream to look for them, especially in areas where water is slow moving or still. The adults are so short-lived that they do not feed, but you may be able to see them in their large 'mating cloud', if you're lucky.

WHEN TO LOOK Spring, summer and autumn.

HABITAT HELP Protecting freshwater areas from pollutants is a good way to support mayfly species.

SIMILAR SPECIES As a precious bait species for fly-fishers, the mayfly might also be referred to as a shadfly or fishfly, depending on where you are. Lacewings (*see* p.153), dragonflies (*see* p.139) and damselflies (*see* p.145) also have similar body shapes that may trip you up when identifying them.

Mallada signatus

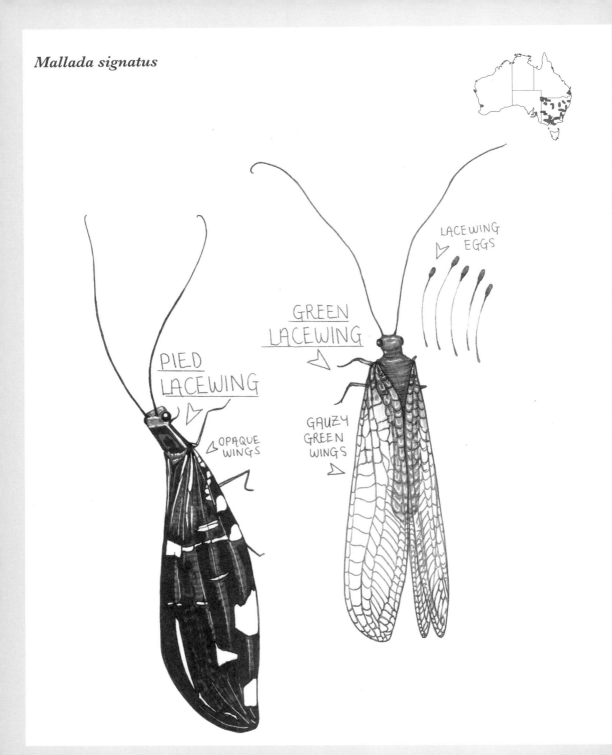

GREEN LACEWING

These common summertime house visitors are so-named for their delicate, translucent wings, but they also go by the edgy name 'goldeneye'. This refers to the metallic golden eyes of these delicate insects and, to match their name, they have very interesting strategies for surviving to adulthood – there's a lot of forward thinking and 007-esque assassination involved (only of aphids, don't worry).

When it comes to reproduction, green lacewings lay eggs that you might have seen before without recognising. The first few times I saw them, I thought they were a fungus or a mould fruiting body. Often I find these elaborate eggs spaced along window ledges or on weatherboards outside the house. It's theorised that the reason the females lay eggs on stalks is so the ravenous larvae that emerge from the eggs don't immediately turn around and eat the other eggs in the clutch. That hungry streak in the larvae comes in handy, however. They are excellent 'biological controls' or 'beneficiaries' to gardeners, as they predate aphids, mealybugs and other tricky-to-manage garden pests that otherwise damage plants. To disguise themselves while seeking out their prey, a la 007, they sometimes carry their half-eaten meals and other debris on their back. This serves as a kind of junkyard camouflage while they cruise into aphid colonies, where they'd otherwise be recognised. Adult lacewings are seemingly gentle creatures. They live for about a month, and consume mostly nectar and pollen from flowering plants, although they often find a way indoors where they perch on walls and ceilings, a little dazed and confused.

WHAT TO LOOK FOR A green, transparent-winged insect (about 15mm long) with delicate wings that extend past the body. These might be mistaken for a pale moth at a distance, but if you get closer you'll quickly notice their long antennae, tiny head with shining eyes, and clear wings. The larvae look like little hairy, brown grubs, and have a pair of fierce-looking (albeit tiny) pincers for mouthparts.

LIFE CYCLE The larvae feed on aphids and other small pest insects. They moult as they grow and, when ready, form a little silk cocoon in which to pupate. They emerge and usually mate soon after, with females laying eggs within the first week of being an adult.

WHERE TO LOOK Green lacewings are most commonly seen in south-east Australia, most often in NSW and Victoria. They are reliant on flowering vegetation and the presence of prey insects for their larvae, so are less common in the hotter, drier central areas of Australia. Look for them in your garden or local park.

WHEN TO LOOK Spring and summer.

SIMILAR SPECIES Mayflies (*see* p.151) and antlions (*see* p.149). Many other Australian lacewings have similar body shapes and habits, such as the brown lacewing (*Micromus tasmaniae*), and the gorgeous pied lacewing (*Porismus strigatus*, pictured opposite).

Eristalinus punctulatus

GUMBAYNGGIRR LANGUAGE
munyurram (pronounced MOO-nyoo-rrum),
('housefly'); *junbarr* (JOON-barr), ('maggot').

WARLPIRI LANGUAGE
yimangi (YIM-ahng-ee), ('fly', 'native bee').

YUGAMBEH LANGUAGE
junbar (JOON-barr), ('fly').

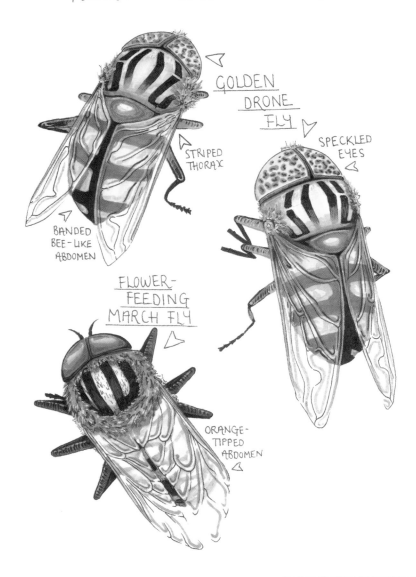

GOLDEN DRONE FLY

STRIPED THORAX

SPECKLED EYES

BANDED BEE-LIKE ABDOMEN

FLOWER-FEEDING MARCH FLY

ORANGE-TIPPED ABDOMEN

GOLDEN NATIVE DRONE FLY

I know what you're thinking: flies produce maggots, annoy you at picnics and buzz incessantly around your head on bushwalks. But bear with me, because some of Australia's native flies are very beautiful, and lovingly feed on flower nectar in native bushland, rather than buzzing over your lunch. In fact, flies such as the golden native drone fly are particularly effective pollinators of plants. With yellow stripes and patterned eyes, this beautiful insect is quite common, but is easily overlooked as it looks a bit like a European honey bee (*see* p.202). These flies, interestingly, are of the same family – Syrphidae – as the smaller hoverflies (*see* p.157).

Like its fellow hoverflies, the golden native drone fly tends to seek out native flowering plants, where it feeds on nectar. Their larvae live in water, sodden mud or organic rich areas of rotting food, where they feed, then pupate away from the wet environment before emerging as adults. If you get a close look at the golden native drone fly, you'll see they splendidly mimic a bee – probably with the hope that any predator will assume that they possess a similar sting to a honey bee. Ideally, their little disguise allows them to get by in an otherwise dangerous world of predators.

WHAT TO LOOK FOR A yellow-and-black fly, about 12mm long, with 'spotted' yellow eyes. The golden native drone fly has tiny antennae at their centre of their head (rather than the longer antennae of bees), and only one pair of translucent wings (bees have two pairs of wings).

LIFE CYCLE Adult drone flies lay eggs in marshy areas. The eggs hatch into larvae (maggots) who live in aquatic environments, breathing oxygen through a specialised organ at the tip of their abdomen. When ready, they pupate, and then emerge as full-fledged adults.

WHERE TO LOOK The golden native drone fly can be seen in south-west WA, in SA, across Victoria, NSW and in Queensland. Drone flies feed from flowers, so keep an eye out on bushwalks, in parks and in your garden, especially during spring when flowers are abundant. I often spot golden native drone flies visiting flowering tea-trees, which tend to have nectar-abundant blooms.

WHEN TO LOOK Year-round, though they are much less common in the winter months.

HABITAT HELP Growing a diversity of flowering plants in your garden is a great way to support this native fly species.

SIMILAR SPECIES Like the golden native drone fly, many native flies mimic bees or wasps (such as the bee fly *Ligyra satyrus*). There is a similar looking and widespread species of introduced drone fly, *Eristalis tenax*, which you may confuse with the golden native drone fly. Other native flies are also colourfully patterned, such as the flower-feeding march fly (*Scaptia auriflua*, pictured opposite).

Melangyna (subgenus Austrosyrphus) viridiceps

WARLPIRI LANGUAGE
ngurrinypa (pronounced (i)-NGOOR-rin-pa), ('fly', 'gnat').

COMMON HALFBAND HOVERFLY

YELLOW-SHOULDERED HOVERFLY

YELLOW BANDED ABDOMEN

COMMON HALFBAND HOVERFLY

If this book offers you a way of learning about the tiny things that share our environment, then one of the tiniest that I hope you'll start noticing is the humble hoverfly. They're often mistaken for little wasps or bees, but are in fact pollen-loving flies. They are excellent fliers, beating their tiny wings incredibly fast, allowing them to hover in space – completely static – as if hanging from a string. They can also cover great distances in flight, especially with the wind at their back, helping to spread the pollen they unknowingly carry plant to plant.

The common halfband, one of the most common and widespread hoverflies, is easily overlooked in the garden, being less than a centimetre long, and so fast-moving they can be hard to identify. However, like bees, birds, and some marsupials, these little critters are effective pollinators in bushland areas, able to creep into the narrow tubular flowers of native species, crawl across the open blossoms of wattles, and visit many introduced species, including common garden daisies. I often see common halfband hoverflies in my backyard, visiting the flowering stone fruit trees, zooming over the grass, or pausing on daisies to take a long snack. They are beneficial to have around your garden, both for their pollination services and for the aphid control their carnivorous larvae offer.

WHAT TO LOOK FOR Tiny (about 7mm long), fly-like insects, with a yellow striped abdomen and black thorax. They are so fast moving, these details can be hard to spot, but as one of the most common species of hoverflies in Australia, there is a fair chance you'll be able to see a common halfband hoverfly, even as they zip about between flowers.

LIFE CYCLE Adult hoverflies lay their eggs on plants, where they hatch into small, wriggly larvae (tiny green, caterpillar-shaped grubs). The larvae have slightly more predatory tastes than the adults, and consume larvae of pest garden species, including scale insects and aphids. They pupate attached to a plant stem or leaf, then emerge as adult hoverflies.

WHERE TO LOOK The common halfband hoverfly can be seen in south-west WA, south-east SA, across Victoria, Tasmania, eastern NSW and southern Queensland. Adult hoverflies eat pollen and nectar, so areas of flowering plants are the best places to look. Usually with a bit of patience and time spent in the park, bush reserve or botanic gardens, these tiny little flies can be seen moving between plants.

WHEN TO LOOK Spring and summer are when the hoverflies are most active, but they can be seen year-round, especially in 'friendlier' climes where flowering plants are still abundant during colder months.

SIMILAR SPECIES Another common hoverfly species is sometimes called the yellow shouldered hoverfly (*Simosyrphus grandicornis*, pictured opposite), which has yellow on the thorax, while the common halfband's thorax is entirely black. Many bees and wasps have similar colouring to the common halfband hoverfly, but are generally larger.

Family Asilidae

GUMBAYNGGIRR
burungan (pronounced BOO-roo-ngun),
('blowfly').

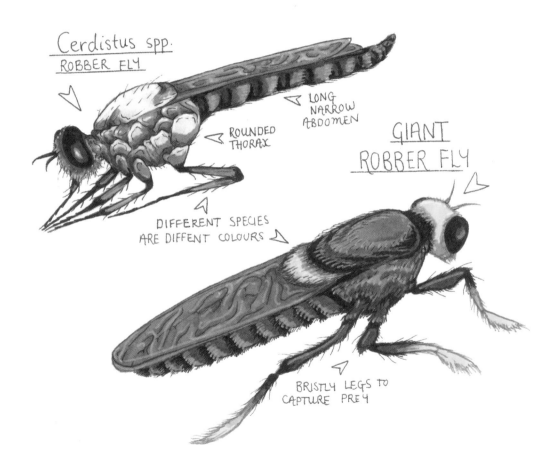

Cerdistus spp.
ROBBER FLY

LONG NARROW ABDOMEN

ROUNDED THORAX

DIFFERENT SPECIES ARE DIFFENT COLOURS

GIANT ROBBER FLY

BRISTLY LEGS TO CAPTURE PREY

ROBBER FLY

The robber fly, à la Hans Gruber of *Die Hard* (1988), is a cold, cunning and venomous thief. Unlike Hans Gruber, the robber fly doesn't want negotiable bonds, but instead is looking for smaller insects to steal and eat. While many of the Australian fly species (10,000 known so far!) consume nectar, pollen or decaying matter, the adult robber fly is instead a predator. They are supremely adapted for their carnivorous needs, in both strategy and appendages, pursuing fellow insects for sustenance. They are fast-flying with streamlined bodies, a strong proboscis (mouthpart) and spiky legs.

Robber flies seek prey by finding an open, high perch from which they can survey their surrounds. When prey is sighted – often a fellow fly or a bee (though some species are known to take spiders and even dragonflies) – they quickly swoop in to grab it. The spiky legs of the robber fly assist in gripping prey. Once captured, the victim is unable to escape as the robber fly gives them a venomous bite, subduing them. Then, the chemicals from the bite do their dastardly work, liquefying the insides of the poor victim, allowing the robber fly to drink them up and leave only the husk of the prey.

WHAT TO LOOK FOR A fly with large eyes, a rounded thorax, and a long, narrow abdomen between a single pair of wings. Some are large (45mm long) and colourful, while others are smaller (approx. 10mm long) and grey in colour.

LIFE CYCLE An adult female robber fly lays her eggs either amongst grasses, in soil or crevices in bark or wood. The eggs hatch and the larvae (maggots) feed on other invertebrates until ready to pupate in the soil, then they emerge as adult flies.

WHERE TO LOOK Robber flies can be seen all over Australia, including Tasmania. Open woodlands and areas around parklands are a good place to look, though they readily venture into more urban gardens. One common place I see robber flies is on fence wires in my local park.

Presumably by perching on the wire, they have an open sightline in which to spot any tasty insects flying by.

WHEN TO LOOK Spring, summer and early autumn.

SIMILAR SPECIES There are many species of robber flies in Australia, found across the continent. Some are large and coloured, like the giant robber flies (*Phellus* spp., pictured opposite), that are about 45mm long; while others like *Cerdistus* spp. flies (pictured opposite) are smaller, 15–20mm, and more muted in colour. Other fly species, such as some march flies, or blowflies, might be mistaken for robber flies. Look for the lengthened, narrow abdomen, which is fairly characteristic of robber flies.

Pelecorhynchus
nigripennis

GUMBAYNGGIRR LANGUAGE
muli (pronounced MOO-lee), ('fly').

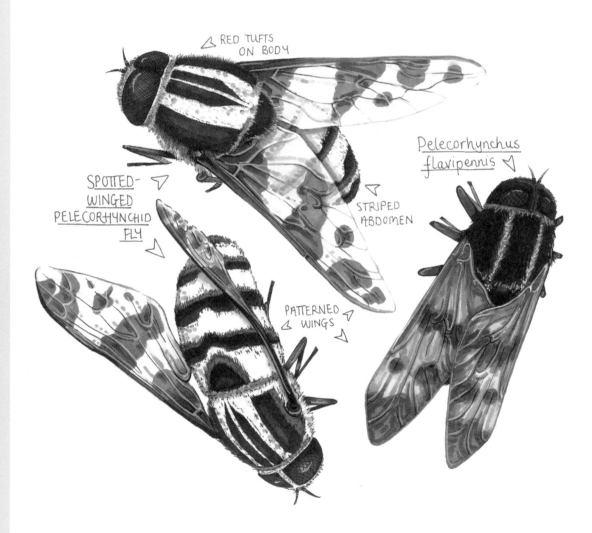

RED TUFTS
ON BODY

SPOTTED-
WINGED
PELECORHYNCHID
FLY

STRIPED
ABDOMEN

Pelecorhynchus
flavipennis

PATTERNED
WINGS

SPOTTED-WINGED PELECORHYNCHID FLY

Feeding on pollen and nectar, often in higher altitudes near marshlands and streams, the distinctive spotted-winged pelecorhynchid fly is not a very common sighting, but it's a memorable one. Like the golden drone fly, (*see* p.155), these patterned insects really make you re-think your insect categories. While most people associate the word 'fly' with a blowfly, bush fly or, at worst, a march fly waiting to take a bite of your unsuspecting leg on a picnic, this spotted-winged species is of a much more delicate sort. These ornate insects go about their days moving from flower to flower, feeding and seeking a mate, with little regard for the activities of us mere humans.

The larvae of this species live in marshy soils where they predate soft invertebrates, such as earthworms, while adults seek out pollen and nectar from tea-tree and other flowering natives along the eastern Great Dividing Range.

WHAT TO LOOK FOR A white and black spotted fly, about 10mm long (not including wings), with pinkish-red patterns at the 'shoulders', base of the thorax, and across the abdomen. The wings are opaque white with black spots. Their bodies have fine hairs, which may sometimes result in the transfer of pollen between flowers.

LIFE CYCLE After mating, a female spotted-winged pelecorhynchid fly lays eggs in a marshy, damp area of bushland. Larvae live in these swampy areas, feeding and growing until they pupate. Eventually, an adult fly emerges to seek out flowers and a mate.

WHERE TO LOOK The spotted-winged pelecorhynchid fly can be seen in Tasmania, and from Victoria to south-east Queensland, though their population is quite sparse, or at least hard-to-find. These flies seem to love tea tree flowers, so going to flowering bush reserves, especially alongside marshy or boggy areas, are good places to start looking.

WHEN TO LOOK Summer.

HABITAT HELP Protecting wetlands and marshlands, especially delicate bogs in alpine areas, is a great way to support insect diversity in these regions.

SIMILAR SPECIES Many flies of the family Pelecorhynchidae are beautifully coloured and patterned insects, including *Pelecorhynchus flavipennis* (pictured opposite). There are about 30 named species of Pelecorhynchid flies in Australia, all with a similar range to the spotted-winged pelecorhynchid fly.

Culex annulirostris

ALYAWARR LANGUAGE
aheny (pronounced a-YINY-a), ('mosquito').

GUMBAYNGGIRR LANGUAGE
guraa (goo-RAAH), ('mosquito').

WARLPIRI LANGUAGE
kiwinyi (KIH-win-yee); *pampula* (BAHM-poo-lah), ('mosquito').

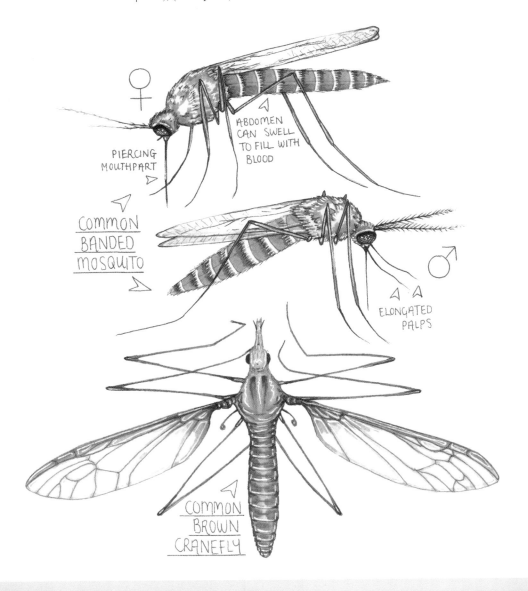

PIERCING MOUTHPART

ABDOMEN CAN SWELL TO FILL WITH BLOOD

COMMON BANDED MOSQUITO

ELONGATED PALPS

COMMON BROWN CRANEFLY

COMMON BANDED MOSQUITO

When I was growing up, one of the moments that stayed with me from *Jurassic Park* (1993) was that little piece of solidified amber, extracted from deep underground, in which a mosquito was trapped. That one little mosquito held the potential for an incredible amount of chaos – and the same is true of modern Australian mosquitoes. Mosquitoes are within the same order as flies (Diptera), and the common banded mosquito is just one of many culprits that may have interrupted your backyard game of cricket.

Despite their infamy as blood-sucking parasites, only female mosquitoes are biters. When piercing a victim with their specialised mouthparts, they release a small amount of saliva, which acts as an anti-coagulant, and allows for the free flow of blood into the mosquito's tummy. This exchange of fluid is the main culprit for the transfer of diseases between humans by mosquitoes. The viruses survive in the salivary gland of the mosquito and thus are transferred into the human body when the mosquito next bites. The females feed on blood to meet the protein needs they have for egg production, whilst males subsist on flower nectar. In my mind, the females are small vampires, fierce and unabashedly thirsty for blood, whilst males, dancing on the breeze to George Harrison's *My Sweet Lord,* are peace-loving hippies, subsisting on flower nectar and good vibes.

WHAT TO LOOK FOR A very small (about 5–10mm length), long-legged fly. The common banded mosquito is a dark-bronze colour with striped legs and bands across the abdomen. The females have a long needle-like mouthpart. Males are of a similar size, but have feathery antennae and larger 'palps' alongside their rostrum (these are sensory organs, *see* opposite).

LIFE CYCLE A female mosquito lays an egg on the surface of a body of water, be it a lake, puddle, or even the water in the base of your pot plants. These eggs hatch and turn into larvae ('wrigglers') that hang from the surface and filter particles from the water for food. Like dragonfly larvae, (*see* p.139), the larvae have a specialised breathing apparatus at the end of their abdomen. These larvae pupate in the water before they hatch into adult mosquitoes. The newly hatched adults crawl from the water to dry and seek out plant nectar to fuel their flight needs. Flying males congregate in large clouds into which females enter and get busy. After mating, the females quickly search out animals to bite and draw blood from to fulfil their protein needs. When readily fed on blood, the females will lay eggs and renew the cycle.

WHERE TO LOOK The common banded mosquito can be seen around the Australian coast, excluding Tasmania (though other mosquito species are common there). They are most likely to be found near areas that have standing water.

WHEN TO LOOK Early spring to late autumn in the south, year-round further north. Populations tend to see a spike in numbers after rains where breeding sites (standing bodies of water) are readily available.

SIMILAR SPECIES The mosquito family is Culicidae, and many species can be seen in Australia. Male mosquitoes are sometimes mistaken for crane flies, such as the common brown crane fly (*Leptotarsus costalis*, pictured opposite), or vice versa.

Didymuria violescens

WARLPIRI LANGUAGE
nyinnga (pronounced NYING-ah), ('stick insect' or 'treeless, dry country').

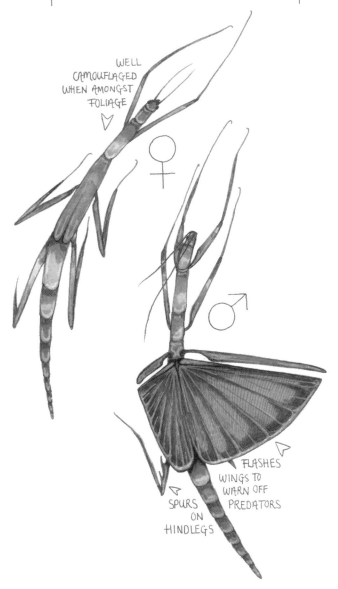

WELL CAMOUFLAGED WHEN AMONGST FOLIAGE

♀

♂

FLASHES WINGS TO WARN OFF PREDATORS

SPURS ON HINDLEGS

SPUR-LEGGED PHASMID

Phasmids go by many colloquial names: stick insects, walking sticks or, in some cases, ghost insects. They eat eucalypt leaves, moving slowly through the canopy, hanging in foliage, relying on their camouflaged bodies and slow movements to hide from prying eyes. If disturbed, the phasmid can flash its brightly coloured wings as a 'startle' display to scare off would-be predators. If you're lucky enough to ever see this display, or to see them in flight, you'll notice the flashy, pink-purple wings that earn them their second name 'violet-winged stick insect'. These rare-glimpsed wings are so delicate and bright, they remind me of a taffeta dress of the 1950s – most specifically, the famous pink dress Marilyn Monroe wore in *Gentlemen Prefer Blondes* (1953). In other cases, especially amongst younger members of the species, if threatened the phasmid will simply drop and 'play dead', a la jewel beetles (*see* p.103) and pintail beetles (*see* p.77). Another stratagem for survival is that phasmids, like skinks, can regrow a leg if one gets plucked off by a predator!

Females generally don't fly, but males can take brief bursts of flight, which is particularly lovely to see, as it reveals their delicate violet wings, which otherwise remain folded out of sight.

WHAT TO LOOK FOR A long, narrow insect, up to about 100mm long, with a greenish body, brown legs and small antennae. Males are more slender than females, and have spurs on their hind legs. The wing colour varies a little, but both males and females can possess violet or pink wings, although it's very hard to spot the wings when they're folded against the body.

LIFE CYCLE The males produce a spermatophore, which is essentially a packet of sperm, which they transfer to the female when it comes time to mate (*see* p.xix). After receiving the spermatophore, females lay lots of eggs to better their chance of their kids (nymphs) surviving to adulthood. The nymphs quickly retreat to tree canopies, where they feed and moult several times until they become fully-fledged adults.

WHERE TO LOOK The spur-legged phasmid can be seen in south-east SA, across Victoria, eastern NSW and southern Queensland. They largely feast on eucalypt leaves, so keep an eye out in local bush reserves, wind breaks on farmland and along watercourses where gum trees grow.

WHEN TO LOOK Summer in the south, and may have longer adult seasons in the north. Usually nymphs emerge in early summer, spend a couple of months maturing, and may persist into early autumn.

SIMILAR SPECIES There are around 100 species of stick insects described in Australia. Some are very similar to the spur-legged phasmid, such as the strong stick insect (*Anchiale briareus*). Others are more spectacularly camouflaged, like Macleay's spectre (*see* p.167), thicker and stouter such as the tree lobster (*see* p.169) or the titan stick insect (*Acrophylla titan*), which is an enormous (about 20cm long) brown phasmid found in Queensland and NSW.

Extatosoma tiaratum

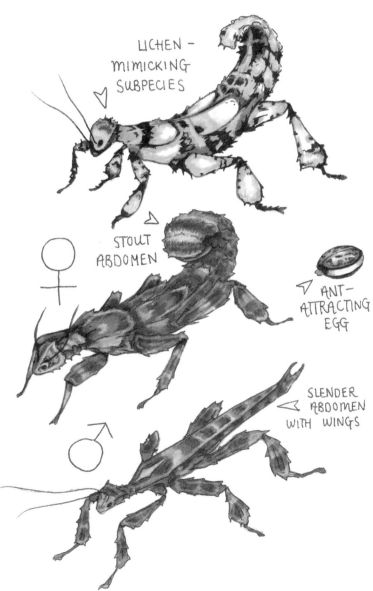

LICHEN –
MIMICKING
SUBPECIES

STOUT
ABDOMEN

ANT–
ATTRACTING
EGG

SLENDER
ABDOMEN
WITH WINGS

MACLEAY'S SPECTRE

Looking like it walked out of a Salvador Dali painting, the surreal and wondrous Macleay's spectre is a truly fascinating insect. Occasionally seen in eastern Australia, they feed on a wide variety of native leaves, amongst which they stay well camouflaged. If you get to see one, you might spot it swaying slightly, mantis-like, which no doubt helps it remain even more hidden amongst the breeze tossed leaves of its arboreal home. Both the males and females look very much like brown, dry leaves or sticks. However, the females also have more spikes, wider body parts, and a curling tail that, combined, make them look especially striking. They are an incredible sight to behold as adults, but the truly mind-blowing part of their life is their baptism-of-fire youth.

After mating, the female Macleay's spectre lays eggs from a perch in a tree, flicking them down to the soil. These eggs have a special outer layer of fatty, nutritious compounds which, like the seeds of some acacia species (another story), are incredibly enticing to ants. Ants will often find a Macleay's spectre egg and carry it down into their nest where the ants eat the nutritious outer portion, leaving the egg itself unharmed. Here, in the dark and protected galleries of an ant colony, the egg eventually hatches into a nymph. The nymphs are tiny, speedy, and coloured red and black, looking very much like ants, ensuring them unhindered passage through and out of the ant nest. After scurrying out of the colony, the nymphs quickly climb nearby trees where they feed, moult and grow into adult Macleay's spectres.

WHAT TO LOOK FOR The female Macleay's spectre is the most striking of the pair, about 120mm long, a brown to light-green colour, with a wide body, and spiky, leaf-like legs. The more petite and slender males grow up to about two-thirds of that length, and are more 'stick-like' rather than 'leafy', like the females.

LIFE CYCLE The female Macleay's spectre tends to be heavier – and therefore less mobile – than the male, so she waits for him to come to her for reproductive efforts. After mating, the female lays eggs, where they hatch either on the forest floor, or in ant colonies where they have been carried. The nymphs emerge to feed, gradually moulting into their adult form. The eggs can remain dormant for a long period before hatching, depending on seasonal conditions.

WHERE TO LOOK Along the east coast from the northern tip of Queensland to the NSW–Victoria border. Though these insects have sparse populations throughout their range, look for them amongst leaves on a bushwalk, in your local park, or in botanic gardens.

WHEN TO LOOK Spring, summer and autumn.

SIMILAR SPECIES Some other stick insects, such as the spur-legged phasmid (*see* p.165), have similar behaviours, but not many other insects look quite as striking as Macleay's spectre. There is also an amazing sub-species, *Extatosoma tiaratum bufonium* (pictured opposite), which specialises as a lichen mimic.

Dryococelus australis

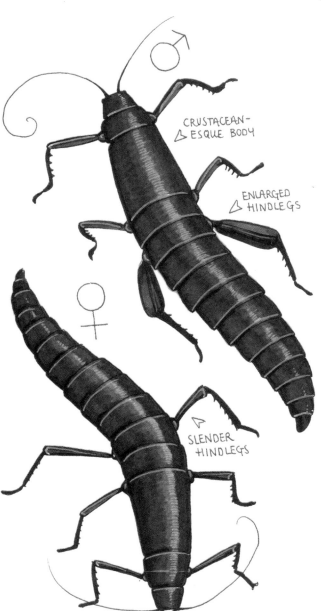

CRUSTACEAN-
ESQUE BODY

ENLARGED
HINDLEGS

SLENDER
HINDLEGS

TREE LOBSTER

Time to go on a swashbuckling journey of survival and reincarnation, a la Chuck Noland of *Cast Away* (2000). The tree lobster, also known as the Lord Howe Island stick insect, was believed to have become extinct back in 1920. Black rats had been introduced to Lord Howe Island, along with human settlers, and the rats quickly predated the slow-moving tree lobster insects to (seeming) extinction. However, come 2001, a small group of hopeful researchers headed out to a jagged piece of rock known as Ball's Pyramid, situated 20km south-east of Lord Howe Island. Ball's Pyramid, which rises 500m above the sea surface, looks like a giant shark fin, petrified into stone in the middle of stormy waters. On this huge blade of rock, the researchers discovered a tiny population of surviving tree lobsters. These insects truly do look like terrestrial crustaceans, making them worthy of the name 'tree lobster'. It's speculated that, much like Chuck Noland washed up on an obscure island, a tiny population of these unique stick insects somehow made their way from Lord Howe Island to Ball's Pyramid, and held on there, surviving on the limited shrubs that grew amongst the rocky crags. (For eighty years, no less.)

A couple of years after their rediscovery, four adult tree lobsters were collected from Ball's Pyramid and taken to the mainland, where a breeding program got underway at Melbourne Zoo. Meanwhile, the eradication of black rats from Lord Howe Island began, with the intention of re-establishing a population of the tree lobsters there. The tree lobster is known colloquially as a 'Lazarus species', a species rediscovered after being considered extinct, a bit like the Eltham copper butterfly (*see* p.19).

WHAT TO LOOK FOR A cylindrical, dark brown stick insect, up to about 110mm long – kind of like a cigar with legs. The females are bigger than the males, while the males have enlarged hindlegs and antennae. They don't have functional wings, so they get around by crawling and climbing. They are nocturnal, emerging after dark to feed and mate, then retreating to hollows during the day to hide away.

LIFE CYCLE A female tree lobster lays her eggs in the soil by nudging her ovipositor (tip of abdomen) into the soil. She then diligently uses her abdomen to smooth over the soil where it was disturbed, covering up the egg. Upon hatching, the nymph stick insects emerge to feed and grow, and moult gradually until they are mature adults, ready to renew the cycle.

WHERE TO LOOK Once upon a time, tree lobsters were so abundant on Lord Howe Island, they were used as fishing bait. Although entirely absent from the island at the time of writing, hopefully in the future Lord Howe Island will once again be a place to see tree lobsters in their natural habitat (visits to Ball's Pyramid are restricted). These castaway creatures were rediscovered feeding from the only shrub growing on Ball's Pyramid (a tea tree, *Melaleuca howeana*), but in captivity they happily feed on a range of both native and non-native leaves. Time will hopefully reveal more to us about these creatures' specific and fascinating life habits.

SIMILAR SPECIES Not many other insects could be mistaken for the glorious tree lobster.

Pseudomantis albofimbriata

ALYAWARR LANGUAGE
antyekanty (pronounced un-CHICK-aintch), ('mantis' or 'stick insect').

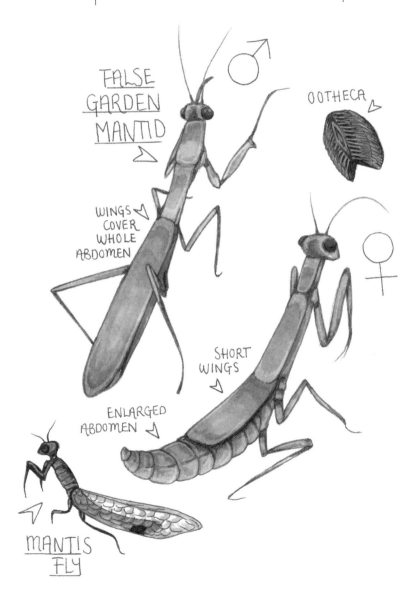

FALSE GARDEN MANTID ▷

WINGS COVER WHOLE ABDOMEN ◁

OOTHECA ▷

SHORT WINGS ◁

ENLARGED ABDOMEN ▷

MANTIS FLY

FALSE GARDEN MANTID

Female false garden mantids are often framed as a kind of femme fatale character amongst insects, seeming to seduce males just to eat them – a kind of *Double Indemnity* (1944) exploitation situation. False garden mantids are predators and, along with their angular bodies, hypnotic slow movements, and rumours of dispatching lovers while in the act, it's easy to see where the film noir creep factor comes from. While, yes, after the romance fades, the male protagonist-mantis is going to end up at the wrong end of a murder case, the habits of the female mantids are a bit more complicated than seduction for the purposes of insurance fraud.

These are solo-living, carnivorous insects that hide out amongst foliage, awaiting an unsuspecting insect on which to pounce (they are often described as 'sit-and-wait predators'). When mature and ready to seek out a mate, a female mantid, unable to fly, lets mates come to her. Finding a perch, she adopts what is known as a 'calling posture'. Moving her abdomen, she releases pheromones that call in males. Once a male is sighted, they seek one another out to do the dirty. In some cases, while the male is distracted, the female starts to eat him, midway through funny business. Female mantids don't *always* eat males after mating, but this habit – called sexual cannibalism – is a strategy for undernourished female mantids to gain resources, benefiting her egg production and prospects for her young. However beneficial, the vision of females biting off the head of the male mid-coitus is brutal, and after this violent act, the male mantid's body can sometimes continue to procreate for a disturbingly long period of time. Sheesh. That said, well-nourished females tend to let the subjects of their trysts escape un-munched.

WHAT TO LOOK FOR A lanky, green insect, about 50mm long, with folded forelegs and wide-set eyes. Most false garden mantids are green, but sometimes can appear brown.

LIFE CYCLE After mating, a female lays an ootheca (egg case, pictured opposite), and goes on her dastardly way, ambushing prey and rubbing those creepy forelegs together in glee. After hatching, teeny-tiny mantises emerge, begin to feed, and grow, undergoing several moults until they reach their adult form.

WHERE TO LOOK On the east coast from Victoria to south-east Queensland. Look out for them in lush healthy gardens and bushland reserves, especially where other insect life is abundant. They can be very well camouflaged, so it's worthwhile taking the time to slowly scan shrubs up close.

WHEN TO LOOK Summer and early autumn, but likely will have a longer adult presence in the more northern areas of their range.

HABITAT HELP Creating a foliage-rich garden with plenty of nooks, crannies and water to support insect life can also support local mantis populations.

SIMILAR SPECIES There are about 120 species of described mantises in Australia. An insect of a different order completely, the mantis fly (*Austromantispa* spp., pictured opposite) about 30mm long, has a very similar body posture and habit, though this species is technically a lacewing (*see* p.153).

Paraoxypilus tasmanienensis

WARLPIRI LANGUAGE
yuljulju (pronounced YULE-jool-joo),
('praying mantis').

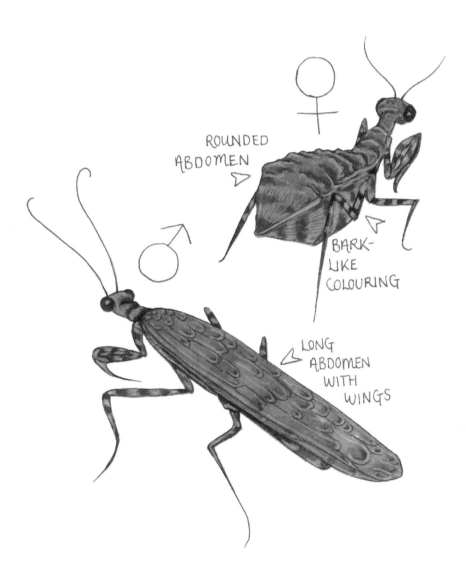

ROUNDED ABDOMEN

BARK-LIKE COLOURING

LONG ABDOMEN WITH WINGS

BLACK BOXER BARK MANTID

Like other mantids, black boxer bark mantids are predators, waiting to pounce on and consume prey as they scurry past. Whilst the false garden mantid tends to hide amongst lush green foliage, the black boxer bark mantid loves to hide on tree trunks, branches, rocks or on leaf litter in bushland, where it can pursue ants and other small prey.

I was lucky enough to see one of these pocket-rocket insects when I was once walking in the Wild Dog Mountains on Gundungurra Country in NSW. It was scurrying along the path and, despite being tiny and quite well camouflaged, it kind of exuded an aura of confident bossiness. They take quick darting runs forward, pause, then continue, much more mobile than their larger, greener mantid counterparts (*see* p.171). Black boxer bark mantids have teeny little arms they keep folded close to the thorax as they move, and they tend to preen themselves at rest. Many other mantids of this genus, 'boxer bark mantises' (*Paraoxypilus*) have cryptic colouration (cryptic meaning camouflaged). If you see a small, brown-and-grey mantis with buff little forelegs, it's likely one of this genus.

WHAT TO LOOK FOR A grey, brown-and-black praying mantid, very small (about 20mm long), looking much like a moving piece of bark. The patterning varies between individual mantids, and the males and females differ a little in shape. The females have a more rounded abdomen, and cannot fly. The males have longer, narrower bodies, and *can* fly. They also have pinkish patches on the inside of each foreleg, though this can be very hard to spot.

LIFE CYCLE After mating, an adult female black boxer bark mantid will lay her eggs in a foamy substance, which hardens into an ootheca (egg case). When ready, nymphs hatch from the ootheca, seek out prey, grow and moult into their adult form.

WHERE TO LOOK The black boxer bark mantid can be seen in south-west WA, south-east SA, across Victoria and Tasmania, in eastern NSW and south-east Queensland.

As they predate other small invertebrates, heading to areas of national park, state forest, bush reserves, or bush-adjacent gardens are good places to start looking. Remain in one spot for a while in case you can see any movement on tree trunks or amongst leaf litter, as these tiny mantids can be hard to spot when they're frozen.

WHEN TO LOOK Spring, summer and autumn, though they may have longer seasons of adulthood in the warmer tropical regions of their range.

HABITAT HELP Protecting bushland reserves will help support boxer bark mantids.

SIMILAR SPECIES As mentioned, other species of the boxer bark mantids genus, *Paraoxypilus*, will be similar in appearance and behaviour. Some other species of mantids are quite effective at camouflaging against bark, such as the eastern bark mantid (*Gyromantis occidentalis*), found in northern and western Australia.

Torbia viridissima

WARLPIRI LANGUAGE
wakupartardi (pronounced WAH-koo-BAH-dar-dee), ('green grasshopper').

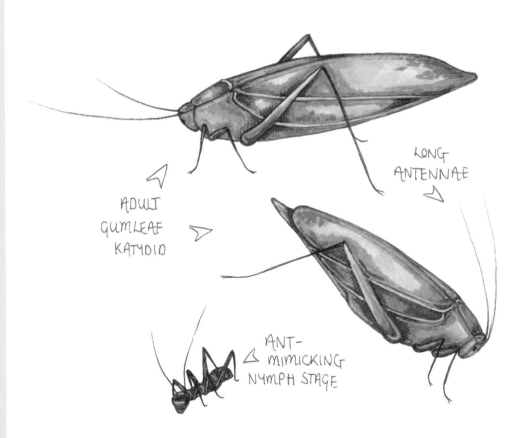

LONG ANTENNAE

ADULT GUMLEAF KATYDID

ANT-MIMICKING NYMPH STAGE

GUMLEAF KATYDID

Meet the gumleaf katydid, a master of disguise. Often mistaken for crickets or grasshoppers, these green critters are actually part of a different family: Tettigoniidae. While katydids look superficially a bit like crickets, these leaf-munching insects are frequent wanderers through tree canopies and lush gardens, and are found in alpine habitats, eucalypt forests, and even rather arid areas of Australia. While some are vibrantly coloured, like the mountain katydid (*see* p.177), others, like the gumleaf katydid, are well camouflaged for their life amongst gum trees.

Though the adults resemble eucalypt leaves, as nymphs they have a different strategy for avoiding attention. The baby katydids are small, with long legs, and are coloured dark brown and red. As a result, they look very much like ants. Thus disguised, they can scuttle over leaves and up tree trunks while remaining incognito, using the same strategy as a young Macleay's spectre (*see* p.167). When it comes to seeking mates amongst the lush canopy, males (a bit like grasshoppers) sound a rasping call to signal to females. Males have a 'stridulatory file' on their leg, which they drag past their wing to create the raspy buzz of a katydid call. The general understanding is that female katydids go for males that can 'sing' well (aka stridulating with gusto).

WHAT TO LOOK FOR A vibrant green, leaf-shaped insect, about 50mm long, with lengthy antennae and long back legs. Sometimes these katydids even have leaf-like 'veins' patterning their bodies. The nymphs, as mentioned, look like ants.

LIFE CYCLE A female gumleaf katydid lays eggs on a plant leaf or branch. A nymph hatches, wingless when they first emerge. They eat, grow and moult into a mature gumleaf katydid with functional wings.

WHERE TO LOOK Gumleaf katydids can be seen in south-west WA, south-east SA, across Victoria and NSW, and along the coast of Queensland. Look after dark, or around dusk, in the warm seasons in your garden, especially if it's well-watered and close to native bushland remnants. Otherwise, look in local parks or areas where

there are plenty of gum trees. These insects are very well camouflaged amongst eucalypt leaves, so it may take some patience to spot one. They tend to be most active at night.

WHEN TO LOOK Spring, summer and autumn.

HABITAT HELP Protecting and growing gum trees in your garden or helping local Landcare to create and maintain bushland reserves can support katydids and, more generally, diverse native insect life.

SIMILAR SPECIES There are over 1000 described species of Australian katydids. Some look quite similar to the gumleaf katydid, such as the common garden katydid (*Caedicia simplex*), while others use different strategies for disguise, such as the twig-mimicking katydids (*Zaprochilus* spp.).

Acripeza reticulata

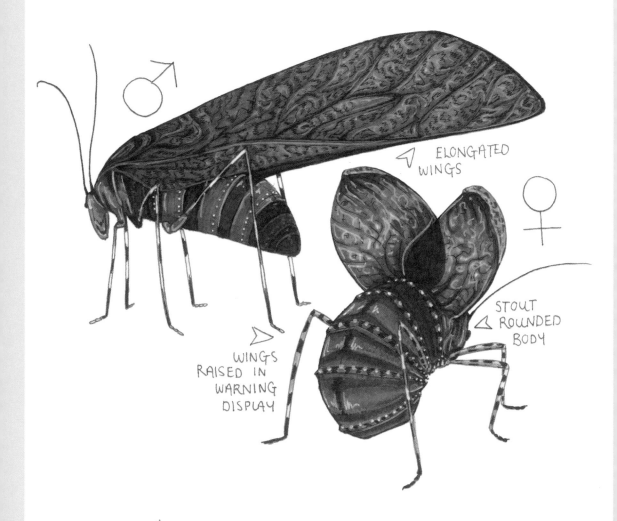

ELONGATED
WINGS

WINGS
RAISED IN
WARNING
DISPLAY

STOUT
ROUNDED
BODY

MOUNTAIN KATYDID

On a walk in Victoria's High Country, I gave my poor mum a fright by screeching gleefully upon seeing a round insect clumsily crawling over the grass trail ahead of us. I had read and heard about the mountain katydid before, but this was my first time seeing it in person, and I was in rapture. Though they are actually fairly widespread, these katydids are most commonly spotted in the High Country, perhaps because those regions have a lot of open grasslands and remnant bushland.

These relatively large critters are brown, with stumpy, rounded bodies and gangly legs (though the males have longer, more leaf-shaped bodies than the females). Their brown colouring means they can be easily overlooked where they wander around mountain grasslands, munching on Senecio daisies. However, if these katydids are disturbed (usually if they are physically touched), they lift their wings and flash a spectacular set of red, black and blue stripes on their abdomen. This is a rare anti-predator display, warning potential threats to back off, hinting that they are not worthwhile prey. As if this brilliant colour display wasn't enough, mountain katydids can also ooze a nasty tasting liquid as another deterrent. These otherwise nondescript, slow-moving insects have an endearingly clumsy walk that contrasts greatly with their bold warning display.

WHAT TO LOOK FOR A brown, leggy spider-like katydid with long striped legs, usually perched on or moving through foliage, or across grasses. Females are about 15–20mm long, with a stumpy, round and flightless body. Males are leaf-like in shape, about 30–40mm long and are able to fly. When these katydids lift their wings their brightly coloured blue-red-and-black striped abdomen is revealed. When not performing their threat displays, mountain katydids can be quite well-disguised, as they are grey-brown, like much of their native surrounds.

LIFE CYCLE Adult females lay several eggs in a secluded spot (often digging a hole in the soil, or laying eggs on stems). The eggs hatch, and the nymphs that emerge are wingless, moving about, eating, growing and moulting until they reach adulthood.

WHERE TO LOOK Mountain katydids can be seen in Tasmania, Victoria, NSW and Queensland. Although they can be found in lowland areas, you're more likely to find them in the High Country areas of Victoria, ACT and NSW. Look in sub-alpine woodland regions.

WHEN TO LOOK They are most common in summer and early autumn in the High Country, though in lower elevations and more northern areas of their range, there are probably earlier and longer flushes of adult katydids.

SIMILAR SPECIES This is a particularly striking species and you'll be hard pressed to confuse it with many other insects.

Monistria concinna

ALYAWARR LANGUAGE
irrkalty (pronounced eer-KALTCH); *ntelty*
((i)n-DILTCH); *menyeynterl* (MIN-yeen-terl),
(terms for 'grasshopper').

GUMBYANGGIRR LANGUAGE:
dirriimba (dee-RREM-bah), ('grasshopper').

WARLPIRI LANGUAGE
jintilyka (JIN-dill-ker); *mikala* (MICK-a-ler),
(terms for 'grasshopper').

YUGAMBEH LANGUAGE
yerribumm (YERRI-BUM), ('locusts').

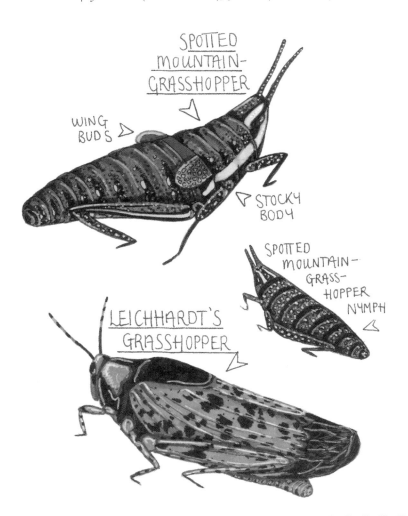

SPOTTED MOUNTAIN-GRASSHOPPER

WING BUDS

STOCKY BODY

SPOTTED MOUNTAIN-GRASS-HOPPER NYMPH

LEICHHARDT'S GRASSHOPPER

SPOTTED MOUNTAIN-GRASSHOPPER

Those of you who have gone walking in the High Country in the warm months of the year have likely spooked many a spotted mountain-grasshopper in the heathlands. These colourful, chunky, banana-shaped grasshoppers, also known as southern pyrgomorphs, love to bask on rocks and amongst grasses in the sun. Between sunbaking sessions, they feast on forbs and shrubs (they especially enjoy mint bush, *Prostanthera* spp.). They are true alpine specialists – and actually have a special component in their haemolymph (blood) that has antifreeze properties. Despite the harsh conditions of the High Country, this special haemolymph means the grasshoppers can survive through winter snowfalls, allowing them to more readily reproduce when the landscape thaws. That said, they are definitely most abundant and active on warm sunny days in spring and summer.

On one November walk at Falls Creek in Jaitmatang Country in Victoria, the grass was *alive* with spotted mountain-grasshoppers, leaping clear of my hiking boots with every step. They have tiny non-functional 'wings', and instead of flying, they hop (really clumsily) between perches. They often don't manage to land on their feet, instead tumbling antennae-over-tail until they right themselves. They are pretty adorable.

WHAT TO LOOK FOR A dark grasshopper, about 40mm long at its biggest, with lots of small yellow dots patterning the body. They have a cone-shaped head, a thick abdomen and short antennae. If you're lucky, you'll see a bright red spot on their stubby wings.

LIFE CYCLE Female spotted mountain-grasshoppers lay eggs amongst heathlands, and the eggs hatch into tiny nymphs. Over a matter of weeks, the nymphs feed on plants, grow and moult their skin as they develop into adult grasshoppers.

WHERE TO LOOK Spotted mountain-grasshoppers can be seen in Tasmania and south-east Australia, and are particularly concentrated in the Australian Alps in both NSW and Victoria. They often hang out in shrubs or in long grass in heathland areas. If you're hiking on the sunny side of a mountain slope, they leap out of the grass ahead of you like a wave breaking.

WHEN TO LOOK Spring and summer are when you're most likely to see these grasshoppers out and active, but they can survive through other seasons.

SIMILAR SPECIES The genus *Monistria* contains several other species (perhaps some yet to be identified) that look similar to the spotted mountain-grasshopper. Many other grasshopper species have a similar shape, but not quite the same colouring. The subfamily the spotted mountain-grasshopper belongs to – the Pyrgomorphinae – are often very brightly coloured. One beautiful example is the rare Liechhardt's grasshopper (*Petasida ephippigera*, pictured opposite), found in the Kakadu region in the NT, which exudes a bad-smelling substance if threatened.

Keyacris scurra

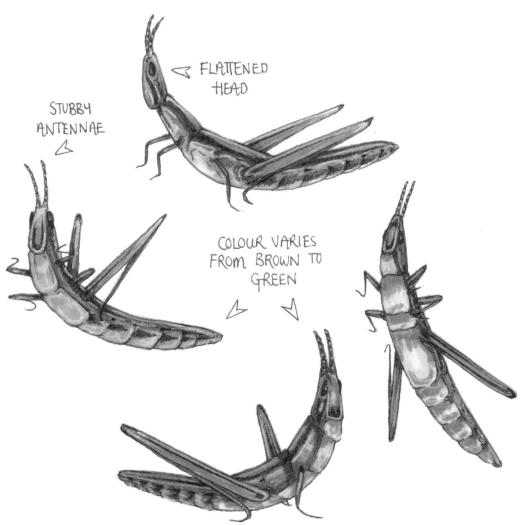

FLATTENED HEAD

STUBBY ANTENNAE

COLOUR VARIES FROM BROWN TO GREEN

KEY'S MATCHSTICK GRASSHOPPER

If there was a symbol for the importance of native reserves in urban environments, no matter how small, Key's matchstick grasshopper is it. These tiny grasshoppers love native daisies and kangaroo grass. They belong to the family Morabinae, which are endemic to Australia, and are very well-camouflaged amongst native grasslands. These grasshoppers were originally famed in the 1950s because they were discovered to have a great variety of chromosomes across different populations, an interesting phenomenon in insect species. They already had limited distribution, and have since fallen further victim to agricultural expansion (wheat and sheep farming, mostly), which has consumed the native grasslands they rely on.

For 40 years, they remained unobserved in Victoria (thought to be extinct), and were only fleetingly glimpsed in select areas of NSW and the ACT. However, a recent resurvey revealed several small populations in graveyards, of all places, and other small patches of remnant grasslands. These oases of Key's matchstick grasshoppers were found across NSW, the ACT and at one site in Victoria near the mountain village of Omeo. While the majority of large patches of native grasslands have been destroyed, it's empowering to know that small regions of unmodified land in unlikely places, such as road verges, cemeteries, railway lines and tiny bush reserves, can become crucial stronghold habitats for endangered species.

WHAT TO LOOK FOR These grasshoppers are tiny – about 20mm long – green-brown coloured, with stubby antennae, and a distinctive up-curved body shape. They don't have functional wings, so that may account for some of their limited distribution (they aren't easily able to travel to new habitats). Females are larger than males, and their colour can vary from fairly vivid green to a pale-brown colour. They have a flat, upright face and short segmented antennae.

LIFE CYCLE Mating occurs in spring, shortly followed by egg-laying amongst soil in grasslands. Nymphs emerge in mid-summer, feed and moult steadily until they reach maturity in winter. These grasshoppers produce only one generation per year.

WHERE TO LOOK In select areas of the ACT, NSW and in very limited areas of the mountains in northern Victoria. These grasshoppers rely on native grasslands, in both urban and non-urban environments, so you could carefully look for them there.

WHEN TO LOOK Late winter, early spring.

HABITAT HELP Native daisies, such as everlasting daisies (*Chrysocephalum* spp.) and kangaroo grass (*Themeda* spp.) are important species that support Key's matchstick grasshoppers – mostly daisies as a food source, and kangaroo grass as habitat. Expanding and protecting areas of surviving native grassland is essential to the survival of this threatened species.

SIMILAR SPECIES Several other species of grasshopper in Australia have a similar body shape, such as the giant green slantface (*Acrida conica*), seen sparsely across all of Australia.

Teleogryllus commodus

ALYAWARR LANGUAGE
lrrim (pronounced i-DEEM); *ltywelty* ((i)ll-CHWILTCH); *rlngarr-rlngarr* (LOONG-ard-a-LOONG-ard-a), (terms for 'cricket').

GUMBYANGGIRR LANGUAGE:
dunggarr-dunggarr (DOONG-garr-DOONG-garr), ('cricket').

WARLPIRI LANGUAGE
Japangardi-japangardi (JAH-pahng-AR-dee-JAH-pahng-AR-dee); *lirrirnpa* (LID-eern-pah), (terms for 'cricket').

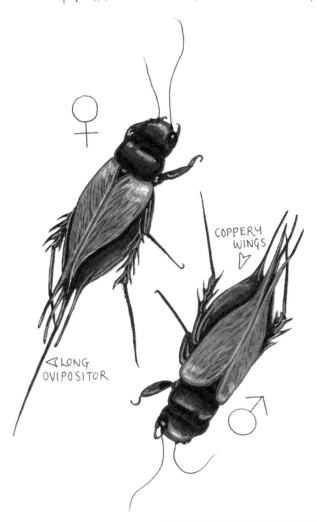

COPPERY WINGS

◁ LONG OVIPOSITOR

BLACK FIELD CRICKET

Alongside cicada calls, surely the sound of the black field cricket is the song of summer. These nocturnal insects are common and widespread, often creeping through front lawns, grasslands, crops and football pitches. Their familiar call is produced by males when they rub their hard forewings together, and they do so to produce two distinct types of calls. One is an advertisement call (the 'yoo-hoo ladies!' call), and the other is specifically a courtship call (the 'wooing' call, that is used once a female has approached a male and physical contact has been made. The songs vary a bit – you'll hear some that are just brief chirps, while others are longer (exhaustingly long) calls. From a male's call, a female is able to discern his potential as a partner. While this sounds a bit like trying to choose a partner from a group of people doing karaoke, crickets, given their success and huge population, seem to be doing something right. Calling males battle it out for both territory and females – they face off both in the quality of their calls, but also physically clash with one another, usually with the goal of scaring off the losing male.

Black field crickets can cause damage to crops when they flourish in large numbers, which may happen when ideal environmental conditions occur (adequate rain, warm temperatures and vegetation for food). They take shelter in burrows to avoid dry spells. When conditions are good, the crickets emerge at night to feed opportunistically on leaves, seeds, stems, fruit and vegetables.

WHAT TO LOOK FOR A black cricket, about 25mm long, with a shiny coppery thorax, long antennae, and large back legs, usually found amongst grass. Nymphs are paler than adult black field crickets and have no wings.

LIFE CYCLE A female black field cricket lays eggs in a burrow, and nymphs hatch to feed, grow and moult several times before becoming fully mature adults. They reproduce rapidly, sometimes producing multiple generations over the warm months of the year, if conditions are favourable.

WHERE TO LOOK Black field crickets can be seen in south-west WA, in the northern NT, Queensland, NSW, south-east SA, Victoria and Tasmania. They are less often found in arid territories, but readily persist in urbanised areas – even in parklands right in the middle of the city. As ground-dwelling critters for most of their lives, the most consistent place I've encountered crickets is in the grass in gardens or parks. When you step through grass, you'll often hear the noise stop when you're close to one (they're shy). If you pause long enough, or move slowly enough, you can usually track down the source of the sound to find one.

WHEN TO LOOK Spring and summer, but the crickets persist longer beyond these seasons if the conditions are favourable.

SIMILAR SPECIES Crickets are part of the family Gryllidae, and many members of this family may be quite similar. Grasshoppers (*see* p.179) look superficially similar to crickets.

Subfamily Macropathinae

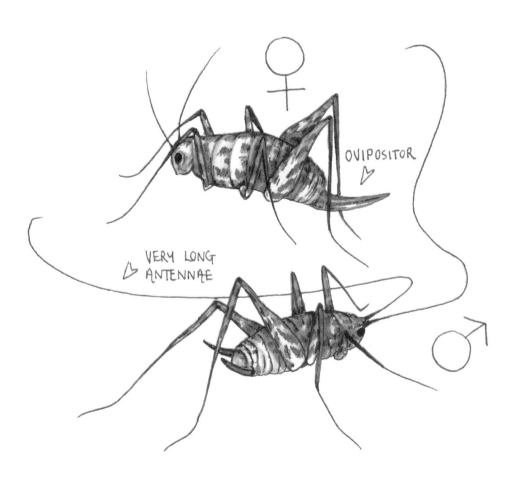

OVIPOSITOR

VERY LONG
ANTENNAE

CAVE CRICKET

These spidery-looking crickets – also known as land shrimp, cave wētā, or camelback crickets – hang out in caves, living out their lives under the cover of darkness. They are within the order Orthoptera, like grasshoppers, katydids, and other crickets, however they are distinct in several ways. They don't produce the chirps that field crickets produce (*see* p.183), nor the rasping stridulations that katydids create (*see* p.175).

Cave crickets are flightless, instead using their long, sensitive antennae to help them navigate the dark cave realm, allowing them to live essentially in total darkness for their life cycle. They do, however, go on brief night-time stints outside the cave to feed under the starlight. Their diets vary, depending on the species, but they are omnivorous, feeding on both organic matter, detritus or other species of invertebrates. By feeding outside, they play an important role in the ecosystems of caves, as they carry nutrients back into the cavern where they are readily eaten by other cave-occupiers, like bats.

WHAT TO LOOK FOR Cave crickets have a rounded abdomen, long antennae and long back legs, making them look quite spidery. The body is usually only 10–15mm in length (depending on the species), but the length of the legs far outreaches the body. They are a pale-brown colour and, being a bit transparent, look like land shrimp. There are even some faint patterns to the shell, like you might see on a crustacean.

LIFE CYCLE After mating, a female cave cricket lays her eggs in a small hole in the soil, using her ovipositor. The eggs hatch, and nymphs emerge to feed, grow, and moult into adulthood.

WHERE TO LOOK Cave crickets can be seen in south-east WA, south-east SA, south-east Queensland, eastern NSW and Victoria, and across Tasmania. They like cool, dark, damp places – primarily caves – but sometimes occur in areas of rainforest.

WHEN TO LOOK Year-round.

HABITAT HELP As most species live within isolated cave systems, disturbance of these areas should be minimised.

SIMILAR SPECIES There are about 20 described species of cave crickets (family Rhaphidophoridae) in Australia, all of which are endemic to particular regions. The Ranga cave cricket (*Parvotettix rangaensis*) is restricted to a single cave system on truwana/Cape Barren Island north-east of Tasmania. Others include the Naracoorte cave cricket (*Novotettix naracoortensis*), found only in a very small region on Ngarrindjeri Country (south-eastern SA), and *Parvotettix domesticus* (pictured opposite), found only in far south-east Tasmania. Other crickets, such as black field crickets have a similar body shape, but are proportionately and habitually different from cave crickets.

Aquarius antigone

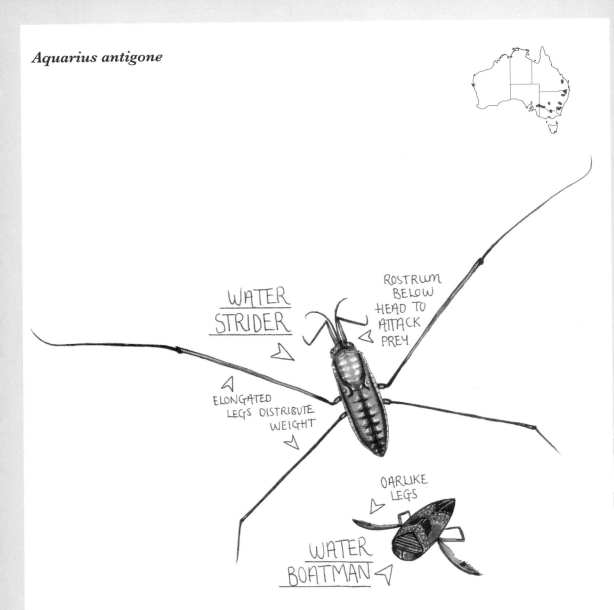

WATER
STRIDER

ROSTRUM
BELOW
HEAD TO
ATTACK
PREY

ELONGATED
LEGS DISTRIBUTE
WEIGHT

OARLIKE
LEGS

WATER
BOATMAN

WATER STRIDER

Water striders are small, surface-dwelling, predatory insects that are marvellously adapted to their environment. Also known as pond skaters, or occasionally as Jesus bugs, they are the fierce, hungry ice-skaters of the insect world. They are covered in multitudes of tiny, water-repelling hairs, and have extremely long legs. They spread their weight across their hair-covered feet, allowing them to remain on the surface without breaking water tension and slipping under. If you look at macro-lens images of pond skaters in the water, you'll be able to see the surface actually bends under their tiny feet – rather than breaking – and holds up the insect. They spend their adult lives skating around on the surface of water, seeking out other bugs as prey (often injured or trapped insects that can't move across the water in the same way they do). It's hard to spot as they move so quickly, but they really do stride with their feet, using tiny, intermittent pedalling motions, as if using skates to slide over the water. Honestly, I wish I could move around on the water surface like they do – it looks like great fun.

There are many different species of water striders in Australia within the family Gerridae. *Aquarius antigone* (pictured opposite) is one of the more common species in the east.

WHAT TO LOOK FOR A small insect, with a body about 10mm head-to-tail, and very long legs, usually perched on the surface of water. Given the long back pairs of legs, water striders can look quite spidery. It's hard to see, but they have a little snout-like rostrum (specialised mouthpart), like the assassin bug (*see* p.191). This is used to stab into the body of the prey insects so the water strider can feed.

LIFE CYCLE Adult female water striders lay their eggs in or along the banks of a water source. The eggs hatch, and the larvae feed, grow and moult, until they develop into adults, ready to breed.

WHERE TO LOOK *Aquarius antigone* can be seen in eastern Australia, but water striders of several different, but similar-looking, species can be seen all over the continent, including in Tasmania.

These insects require slow-moving or even still water on which to 'stride' (skate). They will sometimes find small nooks of still water on rivers or creeks, up against the banks, so these are good places to look. Try your local lake, dam, pond or creek.

WHEN TO LOOK Year-round, though they are more commonly seen in the warmer months in the south, especially if there has been a decent amount of rainfall.

SIMILAR SPECIES Another group of true bugs, the water boatmen (family Corixidae, pictured opposite), are diving insects that are commonly seen in fresh water across Australia. Unlike the water striders, water boatmen spend much of their life underwater. Whirligig beetles (*see* p.127) also live and hunt on the surface of fresh water.

Mictis profana

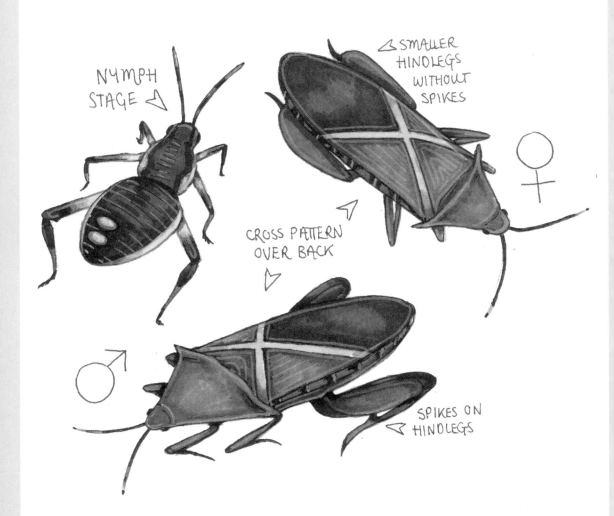

NYMPH STAGE ⤴

SMALLER HINDLEGS WITHOUT SPIKES

CROSS PATTERN OVER BACK

SPIKES ON HINDLEGS

CRUSADER BUG

With a vivid, pale cross over their back – they are also known as 'holy cross' bugs – and a fierce approach to wooing partners and defending territory, the crusader bug is aptly named, easy to identify, and a memorable sighting. These fast-scurrying, plant-feeding insects live and feed on Australian native plants. They seek out mates and defend the best food plants from one another, often with multiple generations of the insect living within close quarters. Crusader bugs have a rostrum (specialised mouthpart) that allows them to suck sap from plants to sustain themselves – this rostrum is a feature common to all 'true bugs' (Hemiptera). Feeding and fighting on a diverse array of plants – from native gums and wattles, to introduced citrus – crusader bugs are common but curious in their behaviours.

The crusader bug is one of the leaf-footed bugs (family Coreidae), so named due to their voluptuous hind legs. In fact, when it comes to competing for the attention of mates, these mega back legs come in handy: males will grapple and try to both smack and squish one another using them. Research papers literally refer to these battle moves as 'jousting', so I cannot help but think of these insects as Knights of the Round Table, defending against the Saxons under King Arthur. If any bug were to pull a sword from a stone, it would be the crusader bug – only they'd do it with their back legs.

WHAT TO LOOK FOR A large bug, about 20mm long, brown, with a big pale 'X' over its back. Crusader bugs have shield-shaped bodies, powerful hind legs and a yellow band towards the tip of their antennae. Males have bigger back legs than females, and also have spikes on these enlarged limbs.

LIFE CYCLE Female crusader bugs lay eggs amongst foliage. After hatching, the bugs go through several stages of growth (called 'instars'). These young crusaders look different in colour and proportion to the adult forms. The growing bugs undergo a final moult to become adults, seek out a mate, and renew the cycle.

WHERE TO LOOK Crusader bugs can be seen across the continent, including Tasmania. They feed on a large range of plants, so look closely on vegetation in bushland, suburban gardens and parklands. I see them occasionally at my local park, where often many young bugs will be hanging out together across leaves and stems.

WHEN TO LOOK These bugs are most commonly seen in spring and summer.

SIMILAR SPECIES The feather-legged assassin bug (*see* p.191), or the gum tree shield bug (*Theseus modestus*), which can be seen across Australia.

Ptilocnemus lemur

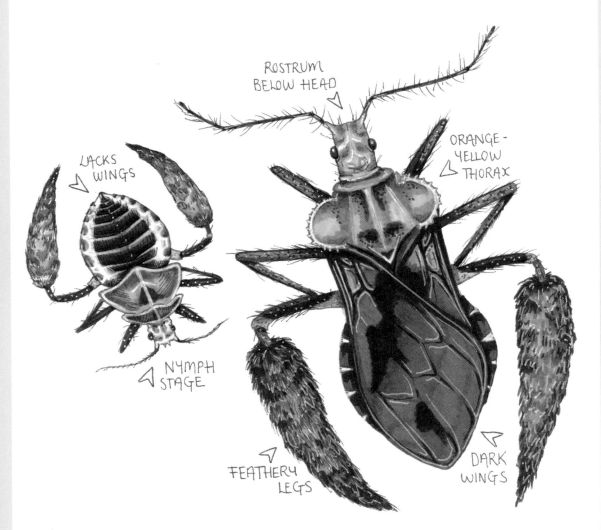

LACKS WINGS

NYMPH STAGE

ROSTRUM BELOW HEAD

ORANGE-YELLOW THORAX

FEATHERY LEGS

DARK WINGS

FEATHER-LEGGED ASSASSIN BUG

Complete with leg-warmers, this stylish feather-legged assassin bug is unique to Australia, and is both a wily and precise predator. As you may have guessed, assassin bugs – family Reduviidae – are insects that predate other invertebrates, including bees, caterpillars, and ants (there are even reports of assassin bugs taking spiders). Assassin bugs possess a rostrum (specialised mouthpart) that they use to pierce their victims, then suck up the contents (shudder). Most assassin bugs hang out in vegetation, where they can creep up on other insects. Truly like assassins, they slowly and stealthily move up close to their victim, then – wham – they stab their sharp rostrum into the insect and start sucking.

The feather-legged assassin bug however, has taken the art of assassination to another level. They have a special gland, known as a trichome, on the underside of their body. This gland produces a chemical secretion that ants love. The ants, drawn in by a sweet smell, blindly clamber right up to the feather-legged assassin bug, who quickly strikes. Their rostrum pierces the ant at a weak point in its exoskeleton – right behind the ant's head, ensuring another meal for the shrewd assassin bug. The young nymphs, however, have yet another stratagem for hunting. When a nymph feather-legged assassin bug senses an ant moving nearby, it lifts one of its feathery hindlegs up and shakes it. The curious ant approaches the waving leg. Then, incredibly, the patient baby assassin bug allows the ant actually to bite its leg. Only *after* the ant has latched on to the bug's leg, will the nymph assassin attack the distracted prey.

WHAT TO LOOK FOR A shield-shaped bug, about 12mm long, with a bronze thorax, and dark wings. The antennae, upper body and legs are sparsely hairy, but the hindlegs are particularly fluffy and long-haired.

LIFE CYCLE Adult assassin bugs lay eggs in a cluster, which hatch into tiny nymphs. The nymphs hypnotise and predate ants, growing and moulting, until they reach full adulthood.

WHERE TO LOOK The feather-legged assassin bug can be seen in south-west WA, south-east SA, Tasmania, Victoria, NSW and Queensland. Look in both suburban gardens and bushland, especially areas where there are plenty of ants. (Though the assassin bug prefers to eat insects, they can use their rostrum to give you a nasty bite, so it's best not to handle them). Incredibly, some of the ants targeted by feather-legged assassin bugs, adults and nymphs alike, are the fierce jumping jacks (*see* p.69), so the assassins aren't limited to more gentle ant species.

WHEN TO LOOK Assassin bugs can be seen year-round, but are more likely to be seen in spring and summer, when ants are more active and the weather is warmer.

HABITAT HELP As with ladybirds (*see* p.101), the assassin bugs in Australia are a part of natural systems in backyards and bush reserves. Avoiding or limiting use of pesticides will avoid unnecessarily wiping out these insects.

SIMILAR SPECIES Crusader bug (*see* p.189). The common assassin bug (*Pristhesancus plagipennis*), found along Australia's east coast, looks superficially similar, though they lack the amazing leg-warmers of the feather-legged assassin bug.

Cyclochila australasiae

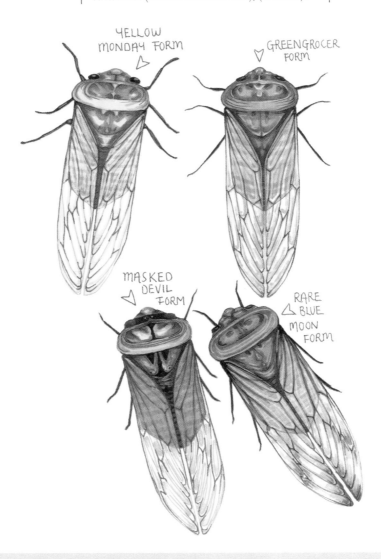

YELLOW MONDAY FORM

GREENGROCER FORM

MASKED DEVIL FORM

RARE BLUE MOON FORM

GREENGROCER CICADA

The greengrocer cicada is the herald of summer. These cicadas are an object of fascination, perching on tree trunks in bushland, and making otherwise peaceful walks deafeningly loud with their chorus of calls. Though exact data on how long cicadas live underground for can be hard to find, in Australia it's likely that nymph cicadas live for several years underground before emerging as adults. They feed on tree sap by piercing roots underground as immature insects, slowly developing out of sight. Then as the weather warms and rain (hopefully) softens soils, the adult cicadas emerge to undergo a final moult, expand their wings, and live out the brief final stage of their existence. The adult cicadas also feed on sap, piercing trees with their rostrum (specialised mouthpart), and using it to suck out the sugary sap to sustain themselves. Only the male cicadas sing and they do so, primarily, to seek a mate.

While it's always magnificent to see a greengrocer, there's also something a bit poignant about it – they're the essence of summer, of noise and heat, but as cicada adults live only a matter of weeks, they are also a reminder of how quickly summer will fade again.

WHAT TO LOOK FOR A large cicada, about 40mm long, including their delicate wings, usually perched on tree trunks. The most common form of the greengrocer cicada is bright green, with some yellow patterning, known as the 'greengrocer'. However, these iconic Australian insects actually have several different colour morphs. The morphs range from the bright-yellow form known as 'yellow Monday', to the turquoise 'blue moon', the 'red warrior', 'masked devil' and even a brown form called the 'chocolate soldier' (*see* examples opposite).

LIFE CYCLE Adult female cicadas lay eggs into slits made in a plant. The hatched nymphs make their way to the ground, where they burrow into the soil and feed on tree sap via the roots of the plant. The nymphs grow and moult underground, until, when ready, they burrow to the surface. As sun-exposed nymphs, they crawl to a suitable place to moult their final nymph exoskeleton, which they leave behind. In summer, you will see these dry husks hanging from trees everywhere, clinging on with little hooked empty feet. Freed of the constraints of their nymph exoskeleton, their wings unfold and harden, their skin matures and they are free to sing for a mate and renew the cycle.

WHERE TO LOOK Greengrocer cicadas can be seen in south-east Australia, with a range extending from Melbourne/Naarm up to south-east Queensland. Stands of native trees near water are the places to look – try your local park, golf course, lake, river or dam where there are plenty of established trees. I have seen them more often on smooth-barked gums, rather than stringybark or rough barked native trees.

WHEN TO LOOK Summer, though populations will fluctuate in numbers and timing, depending on seasonal factors.

SIMILAR SPECIES Redeye cicada (*see* p.195). Several other species, such as the double-drummer cicada (*Thopha saccate*), found in eastern NSW and south-east Queensland, look a bit similar to the various morphs of the greengrocer cicada.

Psaltoda moerens

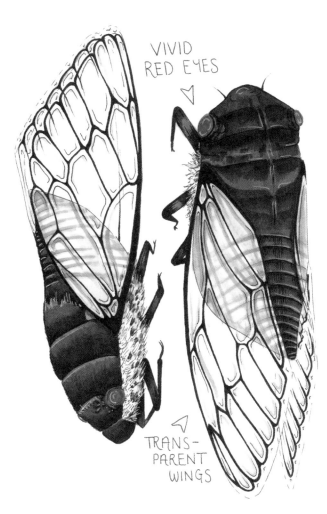

VIVID
RED EYES

TRANS-
PARENT
WINGS

REDEYE CICADA

Ah, the sweet summer sound of cicadas always makes me happy (unless I'm standing right next to a tree filled with them, in which case I'm more likely to clap my hands over my ears). The male redeye cicada, no exception, makes a droning song that alternates with a pulsing, froggy call, which he hopes will draw in a female. Like all cicadas, the redeye has a slightly distinct call from other species, and are most active (loud) on hot days. You'll probably recognise these bugs, either by call or appearance, especially if you grew up along the east coast of Australia. In addition to recognising them, you (as I have) may have been the unfortunate recipient of a spray of cicada wee when passing under an occupied tree. This is actually a sugary substance derived from tree sap that is released occasionally when the cicadas feed. Tree sap has plenty of sugar, and much smaller amounts of protein and other chemicals the cicadas need to survive, so they cope with this by passing out the extra sugar. In many insect species, production or consumption of sugar secretions is an essential aspect of survival, such as the Eltham copper butterfly (*see* p.19).

In the summer of 2020, I was walking on the Six Foot Track in the Blue Mountains of NSW, on Dharug and Gundungurra Country. That year, the trees and air were *thick* with redeye cicadas, taking wing, buzzing between trees, crowding on the long eucalypt trunks, and jostling one another for the best positions. Though there was plenty of honeydew spraying going on, I was simply amazed by the sight (and sound) of so many cicadas so close together. I felt particularly lucky to see so many at once.

WHAT TO LOOK FOR Black-coloured bugs, about 10mm long (in body) with transparent wings, usually perched on tree trunks. The wings are black-veined and are almost double the body length of the redeye. The cicada's red eyes are usually quite visible, out to either side of their head, a little bit like a hammerhead shark.

LIFE CYCLE Adult female cicadas lay eggs into slits made in a plant. Newly hatched nymphs burrow underground to feed on tree sap from roots and grow, until they crawl from the soil, and undergo a final moult to become adult cicadas.

WHERE TO LOOK Redeye cicadas are mostly found in the south-east of Australia, including Tasmania, with a range extending up into southern Queensland. The adult cicadas feed on the sap of native trees, with a preference for gum trees, so native bushland reserves are a good place to start looking. Your best bet is to go to a local river or creek, and scan tree trunks along the watercourse. (Follow the noise!)

WHEN TO LOOK Late spring and summer. Redeye cicadas are subject to the whims of the season and water availability, so some years they may be hugely abundant, while in other years they may be much fewer and further between.

SIMILAR SPECIES Many other Australian cicadas have a similar appearance and habit, including the black prince cicada (*Psaltoda plaga*), found in coastal NSW and Queensland, as well as several other species.

Tettigarcta crinita (mainland) and *Tettigarcta tomentosa* (Tasmania)

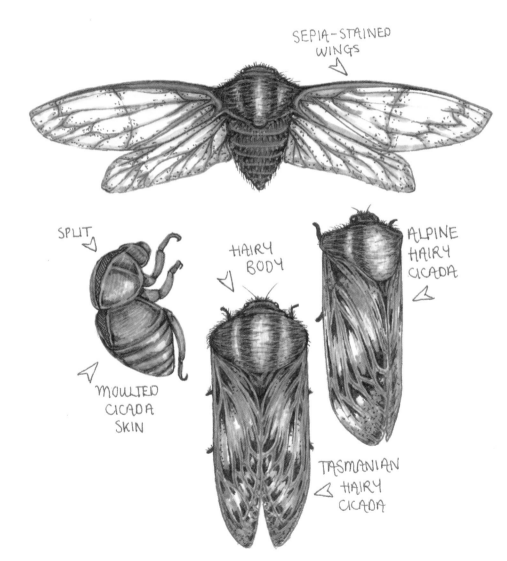

SEPIA-STAINED WINGS

SPLIT

HAIRY BODY

ALPINE HAIRY CICADA

MOULTED CICADA SKIN

TASMANIAN HAIRY CICADA

HAIRY CICADAS

Like a silent film star from days of old, the enigmatic hairy cicada is a relic of bygone times. These cicadas not only look different from other Australian cicada species, due to their fine layer of brown hair, but they also have different behaviours. Hairy cicadas are unique in appearance and lifestyle because they represent the only remaining members of the family Tettigarctidae, which are the most primitive (essentially, eldest) lineage of cicadas. All other species of cicadas – across the whole planet, not just in Australia – are from the only other family of cicadas: Cicadidae. The two hairy cicada species only occur in Australia, which is pretty amazing. Beyond the Australian hairy cicadas, the only remnants of this family are in fossil records, so they really are 'old school' cicadas. The first of the species is the alpine hairy cicada (*T. crinita*) and the other is the Tasmanian hairy cicada (*T. tomentosa*).

These nocturnal insects communicate by vibration rather than an audible call. Most male cicadas have well-developed, large 'tymbals' – almost like an ear drum but on their belly – and neighbouring muscles on their abdomen, which they use to produce their call, the song you hear every summer. However, hairy cicadas have much smaller tymbals and tymbal muscles than other cicadas, and they lack the hearing organs that other species use to hear the calling of fellow bugs. Instead, they communicate through the trees they perch on. The wood carries the vibrations of their calls, allowing them to silently communicate with fellow hairy cicadas.

I was lucky enough to see a hairy cicada up close when walking the Hotham to Falls Creek Alpine crossing, and I was struck by the beautiful stained-glass quality to their wings, which are speckled and slightly sepia-coloured, and truly seem to be from a bygone era.

WHAT TO LOOK FOR A brown, hairy cicada, about 40mm long, including the wings. They have paler markings on the abdomen, and their eyes are close-set at the front of the head.

LIFE CYCLE Female hairy cicadas lay eggs in slits made in a plant. The eggs hatch, and the emerging nymph cicadas burrow underground, where they feed on sap from tree roots. When grown, they travel back to the surface of the soil, clamber up a nearby tree, and undergo their final moult, then emerge as winged adults.

WHERE TO LOOK The alpine hairy cicada can be seen in the south-east High Country of Victoria and NSW and in Victoria's Otways. The Tasmanian hairy cicada is found across Tasmania. As these species are nocturnally active, you may have more luck heading out at night with a head torch and some company, and looking along tree branches and trunks for them.

WHEN TO LOOK Late summer through autumn.

HABITAT HELP As the alpine hairy cicadas are dwellers in alpine country, protecting high altitude areas of natural bushland from drought and clearing – and damage from introduced species, such as brumbies – will help them retain their limited habitat.

SIMILAR SPECIES No other cicada species in Australia has the distinctively hairy body of the hairy cicadas, but the floury baker cicada (*Aleeta curvicosta*), found along the NSW and Queensland coast, is a similar brown colour and size.

Superfamily Membracoidea

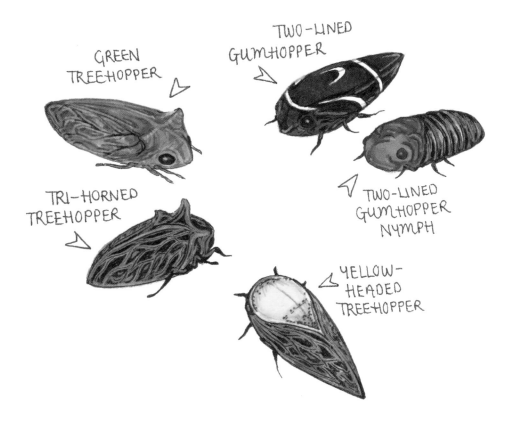

GREEN TREEHOPPER

TWO-LINED GUMHOPPER

TWO-LINED GUMHOPPER NYMPH

TRI-HORNED TREEHOPPER

YELLOW-HEADED TREEHOPPER

GUMHOPPERS

The name 'gumhopper' comes from the way these tiny, shy bugs leap away from would-be predators when approached. If they even get a sense they are being observed, they will often creep around the stem they're on, and hide on its blind side. Despite their shy nature, gumhoppers are worth getting a good look at if you can, as they often have vibrantly patterned wings and groovy body shapes. These bugs occur all over Australia, and are also known as treehoppers (family Membracidae) and leafhoppers (family Cicadellidae). Sometimes certain species of hoppers are termed 'planthoppers' or 'wattlehoppers', but I'm using the term 'gumhopper' as an umbrella to encapsulate the general habits of all of these groups. They are small bugs who have piercing mouthparts they use to 'tap' into trees and drink sap to sustain themselves. They are of the same order as cicadas, Hemiptera, or 'true bugs', and their body shape is faintly reminiscent of their relatives, almost like mini-cicadas.

Some gumhoppers are spectacular, such as the two-lined gumhopper (*Eurymeloides bicincta*, pictured opposite), or the yellow-headed treehopper (*Brunotartessus fulvus*, pictured opposite). Others are more nondescript and camouflage themselves as spines or bumps on plant stems to avoid predation, such as the green treehopper (*Sextius virescens*, pictured opposite), who thrives on acacias, or the tri-horned treehopper (*Acanthuchus trispinifer*, pictured opposite). Like cicadas, many gumhoppers exude excess sugars as honeydew, which ants readily seek out and drink up. Gumhoppers are social, gathering in numbers on their preferred food plants (acacias or eucalypts, depending on the species), where they communicate through vibrations, a bit like the rare hairy cicada (*see* p.197).

WHAT TO LOOK FOR A small (usually about 5–10mm long) cicada-shaped insect perched on a stem or bough, holding its wings in a tent shape over the body. Some are patterned vivid colours, while others are more muted and camouflaged.

LIFE CYCLE Female gumhoppers lay eggs on or in soft plant tissues. The eggs hatch and a nymph emerges. The nymphs feed and grow, until they undergo their final moult into a winged adult, ready to seek out a mate.

WHERE TO LOOK Treehoppers and leafhoppers can be seen all over Australia, including Tasmania. Inspecting tree boughs or trunks in bush reserves can be a good place to look. On one memorable section of walk at Wilson's Promontory/Wamoon/Yiruk, there were so many gumhoppers that they regularly leapt onto my arms and legs to hitch a brief ride down the trail (they're harmless and if one hops on to you, it can be a great chance to study them more closely).

WHEN TO LOOK These insects are most active and abundant over spring and summer but can be seen throughout the year, depending on the species and local conditions.

SIMILAR SPECIES All members of this superfamily, Membracoidea, look quite similar in body shape and have similar habits, but are diverse in their patterning. The widespread pest species, the passion vine hopper (*Scolypopa australis*) is similar in appearance but with bigger, flatter wings.

Family Psyllidae

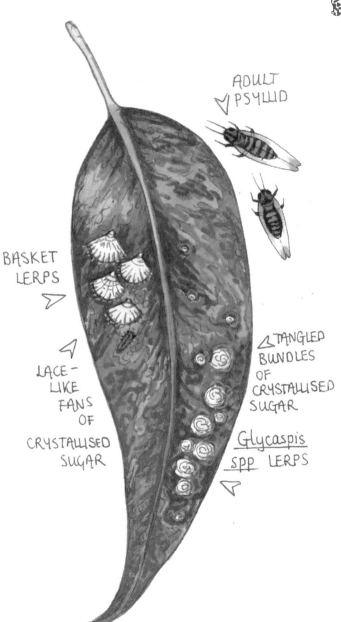

ADULT
PSYLLID

BASKET
LERPS

LACE-
LIKE
FANS
OF
CRYSTALLISED
SUGAR

TANGLED
BUNDLES
OF
CRYSTALLISED
SUGAR

Glycaspis
spp LERPS

PSYLLIDS

Psyllids are teeny-tiny sap-sucking insects that attach themselves to the leaves of native trees. Positioned there, they eat the sugary sap that runs through the trees, much like aphids do. (Sap is largely sugar, produced by photosynthesis. It's like nature's cola. No wonder so many insects drink sap!) When psyllids are in their immature stages, they exude the excess sugars they consume. These sugars crystallise into a waxy, sugary little 'house' on the surface of the leaf, in which they can develop safely. This starchy, sweet secretion is known as lerp. (On occasion, birds, such as pardalotes, bell miners, noisy miners – and no doubt other thrifty species – happen upon lerps and eat them, as they are an excellent source of energy, just like flower nectar.) To add to the wily complexity of the psyllid life cycle, psyllids are sometimes found and defended by ants, who gather about the lerps and drink any excess sugars that these little bugs produce.

First Nations Peoples, including Wadi Wadi, Gija, Kaytetye, Wemba Wemba, Jingulu, Mudburra, Wardaman and Arrernte Peoples have sought out and eaten lerps. Cultural uses vary and have both seasonal and ritual significance to many First Peoples. Some early colonialists also consumed it, describing it as being similar in flavour to the icing on a wedding cake.

WHAT TO LOOK FOR Psyllid insects create lerps which, from afar, look like tiny white dots. Up close, you'll see that they are little cone-shaped 'caps' usually seen in a cluster on a leaf. The psyllids are inside, still slurping away on sap and developing. The lerp caps themselves are usually only a few millimetres wide. The emerging psyllid adults are extremely small still, often about 3mm long, and are little green bugs that look a bit like a flattened leaf hopper. Psyllids are related to scale insects and aphids, and you can see that reflected in the shape of adult psyllids.

LIFE CYCLE Female adult psyllids lay eggs on leaves, preferably young, soft leaves. After the eggs hatch, and the nymphs emerge, they find a spot to feed from and start feasting. The excess sugars they exude crystallise into their little home. Under these lerp houses, they feed, grow and moult until they develop wings and then emerge as adults to seek a mate.

WHERE TO LOOK Psyllids can be seen all over the country, however they rely on native vegetation, so head to a local park or bush reserve to look for them. Look for little white dots on the leaves of eucalypts.

WHEN TO LOOK Year-round, depending on the species.

SIMILAR SPECIES There are several hundred species of psyllid in Australia, some more specialist or species-specific, such as the lilly-pilly psyllid (*Trioza eugeniae*), whilst others will feed off multiple species of trees. Pictured opposite are two examples: basket lerps (*Cardiaspina* spp.) and *Glycaspis* spp. If you get a chance, looking closely at these (or even viewing macro photographs of lerps) can reveal how beautiful and complex these structures are, like arboreal sea shells.

INTRODUCED SPECIES

EUROPEAN EARWIG

GREEN BOTTLE FLY
(WORLDWIDE DISTRIBUTION)

GERMAN COCKROACH

HARLEQUIN LADYBIRD

ELM LEAF BEETLE

GLASSY-WINGED SHARPSHOOTER

SOME INTRODUCED SPECIES:

RED IMPORTED FIRE ANT

MONARCH BUTTERFLY

ENGLISH WASP & WESTERN YELLOW-JACKET

EUROPEAN WASP

ITALIAN HONEYBEE

BUFF-TAILED BUMBLE-BEE

YELLOW CRAZY ANT & TAWNY CRAZY ANT

CABBAGE WHITE BUTTERFLY

COCKTAIL ANT

FURTHER READING AND RESOURCES

ONLINE RESOURCES

Atlas of Living Australia: ala.org.au (app also available). Data used in this book was sourced on 20 May 2022. [Occurrence download at <https://doi.org/10.26197/ala.47f60077-b2f8-48d5-9fae-2f55706226a5> <https://doi.org/10.26197/ala.54316f24-84d7-4411-8501-03a040d3a779> and <https://doi.org/10.26197/ala.7bf3c82f-c96d-4435-8393-599e35e39e5c>]

Australian Institute of Aboriginal and Torres Strait Islander Studies (AIATSIS) map of Indigenous Australia: aiatsis.gov.au/explore/map-indigenous-australia

iNaturalist: inaturalist.ala.org.au (app also available)

State Wide Integrated Flora and Fauna Teams (SWIFFT): swifft.net.au (Victoria only)

FIELD GUIDES

Braby, Michael F. (2016), *The Complete Field Guide to the Butterflies of Australia*, CSIRO Publishing, Australia.

Brock, Paul D. & Hasenpusch, Jack W. (2009), *The Complete Field Guide to Stick and Leaf Insects of Australia*, CSIRO Publishing, Australia.

Common, Ian F. B. (1963), *Australian Moths*, Jacaranda Press, Australia.

Cranney, Kate, Bekessy, Sarah & Mata, Luis (2017), *The Little Things that Run the City*, City of Melbourne, Australia.

Horne, Paul & Crawford, Denis (2015), *Backyard Insects* (2nd edn), Miengunyah Press, Australia.

Houston, Terry (2018), *A Guide to the Native Bees of Australia*, CSIRO Publishing, Australia.

Orr, Albert & Kitching, Roger (2010), *The Butterflies of Australia*, Allen & Unwin, Australia.

Rentz, David (2014), *A Guide to the Cockroaches of Australia*, CSIRO Publishing, Australia.

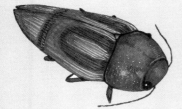

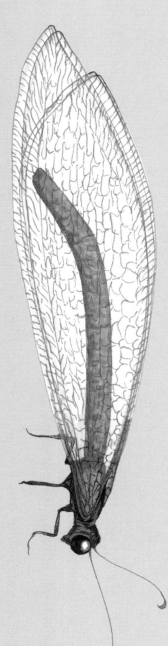

Rentz, David (2010), *A Guide to the Katydids of Australia*, CSIRO Publishing, Australia.

Theischinger, Günther, Hawking, John & Orr, Albert (2021), *The Complete Field Guide to Dragonflies of Australia*, CSIRO Publishing, Australia.

Zbrowski, Paul & Edwards, Ted (2007), *A Guide to Australian Moths*, CSIRO Publishing, Australia.

PAPERS

Braby, Michael F., 2018, 'Threatened species conservation of invertebrates in Australia: an overview', *Austral Entomology* 57.

Braby, Michal F. & Armstrong, J.J., 2018, 'Observations on the ecology of the silky hairstreak', *Pseudalmenus chlorinda* (Blanchard, 1848), *Australian Entomologist* 45(2).

Faast, Renate et al, 2020, 'Indigenous Use of Lerps in Australia: So Much More Than a Sweet Treat', *Journal of Ethnobiology* 40(3).

Kearney, Michael & Hoffmann, Ary, (2019) 'Rediscovering a 'lost' species: Key's matchstick grasshopper', Pursuit, University of Melbourne (Accessed May 2022), pursuit.unimelb.edu.au/articles/rediscovering-a-lost-species.

Mumaw, Laura & Mata, Luis, 2021, 'The socio-ecological benefits of wildlife gardening'. Report prepared for Gardens for Wildlife Victoria.

New, Tim R., 2018, 'Book review: Splendid Ghost Moths and Their Allies. A Revision of Australian Abantiades, Oncopera, Aenetus, Archaeoaenetus and Zelotypia (Hepialidae)' by Thomas J. Simonsen, *Austral Entomology* 57(3).

Pierce, Naomi E. et al., 2002, 'The ecology and evolution of ant association in the Lycaenidae', *Annual Review of Entomology* 47.

Richter, Annett et al, 2013, 'Moths in fragments: insights into the biology and ecology of the Australian endangered golden sun moth *Synemon plana* (Lepidoptera: Castniidae) in natural temperate and exotic grassland remnants', *Journal of Insect Conservation* 17(6).

Si, Aung & Turpin, Myfany, 2015, 'The Importance of insects in Australian Aboriginal society: a dictionary survey', *Ethnobiology Letters* 6(1).

Yen, Alan L., 2012, 'Edible insects and management of country', *Ecological Management & Restoration* 13(1).

ABOUT THE AUTHOR

Georgia Angus is an author, artist and nature nerd who lives on the lands of the Kulin Nation in south-east Australia. She splits her time between studying environmental science, writing and bushwalking. Her first book, *100 Australian Birds* was published by Hardie Grant Explore in 2021.

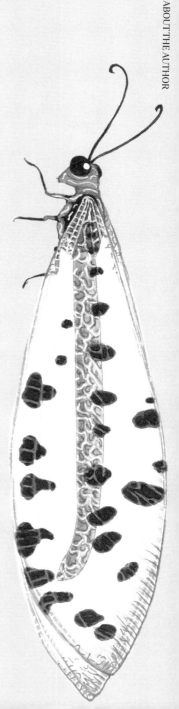

ACKNOWLEDGEMENTS

Many generous people have supported the writing and illustrating of this book. Thanks to the *Atlas of Living Australia* for compiling so much important data, and giving me permission to create distribution maps for the book. Thanks Cameron Begley, Clare Nance, and Jason Caruso for putting me in touch with some brilliant experts. Martin Lagerwey, thank you for providing your photographs as reference images for my illustrations. Thanks also to Don-Herbison Evans and Iona Okey for allowing me to refer to their personal photographs.

Thank you to the team at Muurrbay Co-op, who generously contributed words in Gumbaynggirr language for the book. (Thank you Bron Peddington-Webb for enduring my many emails.) Thanks to the Australian Society for Indigenous Languages for supplying words in Alyawarr and Warlpiri, and to David Blackman for liaising with me and providing pronunciation guides. Many thanks to Faith Baisden for seeking out and providing words in Yugambeh.

Thanks to the team at the Australian National Insect Collection at CSIRO, who kindly tolerated my endless naïve questions and showed me many brilliant specimens. David Yeates, thank you for endearing flies to me, and answering many of my questions. Thanks to Olivia Evangelista for being both a patient and brilliant entomological tour guide. Thank you Michael Braby for drawing my attention to some distinctive species and for sharing your expertise regarding Australian butterflies. Thanks to David Rentz for answering my many cockroach and earwig-related questions. Kate Umbers, thank you for sharing your wisdom about several insect species, including the marvellous mountain katydid and spotted mountain grasshopper, and for being so generous with your time and encouragement. Luis Mata, thank you for being so supportive and generous to a complete amateur such as myself, including reviewing entries, directing me to research and providing your *Gardens for Wildlife* report. Head online to luismataresearch.wordpress.com for more information on Luis' brilliant work.

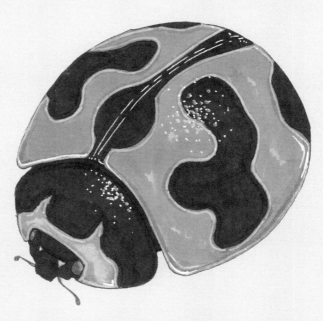

Thanks to the team at Hardie Grant for their support. Melissa Kayser, thank you for believing in my capabilities. Amanda Louey, thank you for helping me piece together the different pieces of the book and for accepting moths into your heart (at least a little bit more than you did before). Many thanks to Alice Barker for her sage edits (and for appreciating my daggy sense of humour). Kate Kiely, thank you for your proofreading efforts, thank you Kerry Cooke for your typesetting, and Jamil Tye for your guidance. Thanks to Michelle Mackintosh for her book design and Emily Maffei and Claire Johnston for the maps.

Many thanks to Dr. Bryan Lessard for his generous foreword, and for sharing his important entomological research with the world.

Thanks to Vera Humennyj, Sean Jameson, and Yss Humennyj-Jameson for your constant encouragement and support. Orien Humennyj-Jameson, thank you for your endless enthusiasm for creepy crawlies, for understanding my hermit ways and for reassuring me when I doubted the validity of writing about praying mantis sex.

Immeasurable thanks to my parents, Leecia and Stephen Angus, and my sister, Kate Angus, for keeping me afloat during hard yards of researching and writing. I can't describe my absurd luck in scoring a family this supportive and wonderful.

INDEX

Alyawarr and Warlpiri names were provided by the Australian Society for Indigenous Languages (AuSIL). The Alyawarr region is located in north-eastern central Australia, and includes country crossed by the Sandover River, which, after heavy rains, flows in a north-easterly direction towards Queensland. Alyawarr country extends towards the Plenty Highway in the south and the Barkly Highway in the north. Warlpiri country is located in the Tanami Desert, east of the Northern Territory-Western Australia border, west of the Stuart Highway and Tennant Creek, Northern Territory, and northwest of Alice Springs.

Gumbaynggirr names were provided by Muurrbay Aboriginal Language and Culture Co-operative in Nambucca Heads, New South Wales. The Gumbaynggirr nation is located on the Mid North Coast of New South Wales. Its southern edge is the Nambucca River, its western edge lies in the Great Dividing Range, and its northern edge is the Clarence River.

Yugambeh names were provided by Faith Baisden whose research was supported by the Yugambeh Museum Language and Heritage Research Centre. Yugambeh language is spoken by the traditional custodians of the land located in south-east Queensland now within the Logan City, Gold Coast and Scenic Rim regions.

Published in 2023 by Hardie Grant Explore, an imprint of Hardie Grant Publishing

Hardie Grant Explore (Melbourne)
Wurundjeri Country
Building 1, 658 Church Street
Richmond, Victoria 3121

Hardie Grant Explore (Sydney)
Gadigal Country
Level 7, 45 Jones Street
Ultimo, NSW 2007

www.hardiegrant.com/au/explore

Assistance with research: The publisher would like to thank Atlas of Living Australia (ALA) for assistance with the data and information to produce the maps in this book. This online resource collates and makes available biodiversity information to the public. Data is provided to the ALA by citizen scientists, professional scientists, museum records and from a variety of research and conservation projects. Distribution maps for this book were created using ALA data in May, 2022, and are intended only as a broad guide to distribution of species. The distribution patterns of species will vary over time.

A catalogue record for this book is available from the National Library of Australia

100 Australian Butterflies, Bees, Beetles and Bugs
ISBN 9781741177978

10 9 8 7 6 5 4 3 2 1

Publisher
Melissa Kayser

Project editor
Amanda Louey

Editor
Alice Barker

Editorial assistance
Gemma Taylor and Jenny Varghese

Proofreader
Kate Kiely

First Nations consultant
Jamil Tye, Yorta Yorta

Design
Michelle Mackintosh

Cartographer
Claire Johnston

Typesetting
Kerry Cooke

Index
Max McMaster

Production coordinator
Simone Wall

Colour reproduction by Splitting Image Colour Studio

Printed and bound in China by LEO Paper Products LTD.